DATE DUE

DEC 4	APR 2		
JAN 13	SEP 30		
JAN 28	NOV 13		
FEB 25	APR 2 / MAY 17		
NOV 1	SEP 27		
NOV 16	MAY 15		
NOV 18	JAN 24		
JAN 17	FEB 7		
FEB 7	APR 24		
FEB 6	SEP 28		
MAR 13	JAN 24		
MAY 22	MAR 11		
JAN 24	FEB 10		
JAN 24	NO 06 '01		
JAN 24			
JAN 24			
JAN 24			
JAN 24			

GAYLORD PRINTED IN U.S.A.

LONE STAR LEADER

Sam Houston

BORN: March 2, 1793

DIED: July 26, 1863

Sam Houston led Texas out of Mexican bondage, avenged the massacre of the Alamo and became the young republic's first president. Before that, he had had a tempestuous career as senator, lawyer and Governor of Tennessee. As statesman and general he adventured in two worlds—that of political Washington and the wild frontiers of the West. In this candid biography, the author reaches past the mist of legend and recreates the man as he was—a passionate patriot who thrived on danger and excitement.

BOOKS BY CURTIS BISHOP

THE FIRST TEXAS RANGER
Jack Hays

LONE STAR LEADER
Sam Houston

LONE STAR LEADER

SAM HOUSTON

by Curtis Bishop

Julian Messner, Inc. New York

97-Biog
Hou

Published by Julian Messner, Inc.
8 West 40 Street, New York 18

Published simultaneously in Canada
by The Copp Clark Publishing Co. Limited

THIRD PRINTING, 1962

Printed in the United States of America

Library of Congress Catalog Card No. 61-7994

Contents

To Brian

★ 1

Sam Finds Kindred Spirits

SAM HOUSTON SAW THE CONESTOGA AND BROKE INTO A dead run. The new wagon meant only one thing: his mother was finally ready to travel across the Big Smoky Mountains into Tennessee. The long-awaited move of the Houston family was at hand.

He caressed the vehicle's gleaming sides, chortling softly. This was a genuine Conestoga, not an imitation. Its blue bed curved up at both ends; this wagon could be floated across streams without unloading its cargo. Its underside was a brilliant red and its canvas bow a glittering white. Had his late father suggested its colorings? Sam could easily believe it. Major Samuel Houston would have wanted his family moving west in a red, white and blue wagon.

The voice of an older brother stopped Sam's singsong momentarily. "Where have you been all day?" demanded John. "You're not about to duck out of all *this* work."

John was three years older, but stood no taller than the fourteen-year-old Sam. None of his five elder brothers did, though all were strong, strapping young men. Sam was unusually tall. Three ax-handles high, said his brothers, and every bone a shiftless one.

"What's to be done?" asked Sam. "If we're really moving, I'll help. Sure I will."

"Sure," John said sourly. "It suits you." Like his younger brother, he wore snug homespun shirt and breeches. No matter what sizes she bought, grumbled the widow of Major Samuel Houston, her sons' garments were too small after one washing.

John studied Sam disapprovingly. The older Houston boys were actually fond of the towering Sam despite his shirking of household and barnyard chores. John privately admitted that his father's namesake could "charm birds out of the trees." Sam could get things done, too, when he set his mind to it. Sam would be a real help for a change. He was eager for this move from a fading Virginia plantation to new land in Tennessee. Especially in a red, white and blue Conestoga wagon. Oh, grunted John, Sam would really hump now.

Mistress Elizabeth Houston hurried out of the house as John and Sam started to lift her spinning wheel into the new vehicle. Not one thing, she said sharply, would be loaded without her say-so. They had a million things to do before it was time to pack either wagon. They had meat to jerk, new potatoes to dig, livestock to feed. "You, John, slop the pigs. And you, Sam, pick a bag of that wild mustard seed. We'll need greens for the table in Tennessee. If I know you boys, you won't leave your appetites behind in Virginia."

Both sons shuffled to obey. Elizabeth Houston was more indulgent than most mothers, but she could lay down the law when she chose. She had been born Elizabeth Paxton, a daughter of Squire John Paxton. She was reckoned "quality" in Virginia, a very socially conscious country in the latter half of the eighteenth century. She had married Samuel Houston in her eighteenth year and had done her best to make his schemes work. Few had. Aaron Burr's vision of a new western empire had gone up in smoke, losing money for such backers as Major Houston, who was a successful father and militia leader but no wise investor. Another few thousand dollars disappeared when Cyrus McCormick produced a better wheat-cutting machine than the one the major's blood cousin had hoped would make them rich. Samuel Houston died in 1806 a relatively poor man. He left his fifty-year-old widow with nine children, four hundred and nineteen acres of land on the Tennessee frontier, and five Negro slaves—an estate valued at about thirty-six hundred dollars.

It was quite a comedown for the daughter of a Paxton. She was taking her brood to a new frontier because her means didn't allow them to live in Virginia. But she wasn't dismayed at the necessity of frugal management. She knew how to make pennies count, and to do without things that weren't absolute necessities. She wouldn't have spent so much "hard" money for a new Conestoga except for one thing.

Sam's guess was exactly right. Major Houston had wanted it.

The million things to be done before even starting to pack—closer to two million—made the impatient Sam fume. His mother seemed to think they were moving to the end of the world. He lost count of the items she called her "possibles"—beeswax and extra-large needles, the camphor bottle in its muslin wrapping, yellow calico she hadn't cut into yet and probably never would, a sadiron heavier than it looked, the best seeds from the garden, the tall kitchen clock imported from England, a bulky walnut bureau which Paxton and John bolted to the Conestoga's bed. Dried turnip greens and squash, eggs packed in cornmeal—then, at the last moment, two coupling pins. "What in tarnation for?" demanded James when Paxton relayed the command.

"River crossings, she says. Reckon she doesn't trust that shiny wagon to turn water."

"It'll float anything between here and Tennessee," said James with a grunt. "You'd think we were heading for the Louisiana Territory instead of just the other side of Cumberland Gap."

That was where Major Houston had located "God's country," some twenty miles from Knoxville along an old Indian trace. The nearest settlement was Maryville, the seat of government of Blount County. Cousins James and John Houston had crossed the Smokies following the Revolutionary War. Sam looked forward to meeting them in the flesh—them and another cousin, also named Samuel Houston, a minister and Greek scholar as well as luckless inventor. This pioneer trio had built Jim Houston's fort to hold off menacing Indians and had helped John Sevier organize the Free State of Franklin. Sam could be enthusiastic about knowing such relatives after the rather colorless cousins in Virginia—Paxtons, mostly, who worried more about cotton and tobacco prices than America's western destiny.

"Can I drive the new wagon?" It took Sam several days to muster the nerve to ask. He was sure of his mother's answer even before he asked the question. He never doubted her affection; but she placed more reliance on his brothers, even the younger William.

Her decision was—as Sam had expected—he couldn't drive the new wagon. John climbed into the Conestoga's seat and cracked a long whip over five stout horses. Paxton drove the older, less pretentious wagon. Sam could ride in either, or walk. Each had its drawbacks. If he walked, ruled his mother, he must keep within her sight. Riding was uncomfortable, since neither tailgate could be lowered.

Most of the time he walked, striding ahead of the two lumbering vehicles. He could pretend that it was his responsibility to choose a path for the small caravan, to decide which distant pass offered the easiest going. He studied the thickets ahead for signs of hostile Indians. "Sometimes, Samuel Houston," scolded his mother, "you're like a child." He didn't consider it childlike to imagine people and events. His father had done it. Major Samuel Houston had believed in a United States of the future which extended beyond the Mississippi River.

So did his son. Wasn't each meandering creek an invitation, and every new horizon a challenge? To Sam, yes. He strained under the burden of their unsolved mysteries. Didn't warlike Indians prowl these hills? Mustn't they be alert to danger every minute of daylight? When would he see signs of the great game creatures—deer, bear, wild turkey? He watched the treetops eagerly, hoping to get a fleeting glimpse of an eagle.

He was tired by sundown, but more because of their snail-like pace than from physical fatigue. It wore on him to keep holding back, to stop and wait again and again.

None of them slept soundly that first night. Paxton and John hobbled the nine horses and set pickets for the cows. William and Mary milked the gentle creatures and filled a tin pan for the two excited dogs. Paxton started the campfire by shooting a piece of cotton from his rifle, with a bit of punk. The quick blaze sputtered, struggled, then decide to burn. Sam took out his jackknife and whittled a pine sliver into the shape of a horse. Little

Eliza Ann squealed with delight at the present. By much scolding and bustling, Mistress Houston quieted them all by eight o'clock, even John and Paxton. By daylight she trusted her elder sons; she must. But come dark, she treated all alike—as children.

Tennessee! Sam could not tell exactly when they reached the new state. There was no telltale landmark of Virginia's limits, or of Tennessee's beginning. The next tier of rugged mountains seemed exactly like the one behind. The trail wound on and on, never an actual road anywhere, but easy to follow. A small dust cloud behind them formed into a procession of four plodding teams, each pulling families toward the new country. Elizabeth Houston firmly declined to join the caravan. They'd make out, she said. Sam could guess why she refused. His mother did not think of herself and her children as ordinary pilgrims. Wasn't she a Paxton herself, and that proud heritage blended with equally proud Scottish ancestry? On his father's side Sam was descended from Highland baronets.

They were not received as common travelers in Knoxville, either. Friendly, hospitable folk were expecting James Houston's kin from beyond the Smokies. Mrs. Houston and her three daughters slept in a great feather bed while her six sons shared quilt pallets.

They were moving again at daybreak. Maryville was fifteen miles away, a hard day's travel; the land chosen by Major Houston was ten miles farther on. Sam stopped several times to look back at Knoxville, the village capital of Tennessee. Here in this mountainous nowhere, he mused, strong and fearless men had formed their own government. One of those distant, hazy rises was Kings Mountain, where the sturdy emigrants from Scotland had slaughtered British redcoats. From this mountain village John Sevier had issued his defiance to the authorities of North Carolina. The settlers west of the Smokies would accept jurisdiction of the United States on their own terms. The compromise, thought the gangling, awkward boy, had been fair enough. The proud settlers had surrendered their chosen name but not their independence. Tennessee or Franklin—what difference did it make what the new state was called? The spirit was the thing that actually mattered, their honor. Sam was more touchy about honor than most boys his age. Six years later he was to receive his proudest possession—a gold ring with that word inscribed in Latin.

The old Indian trace was rough going. They called it a Cherokee trace at Knoxville; that meant nothing to Sam. He did not know one Indian from another. He thought them all savages, born enemies who should be killed on sight. He was disappointed to learn at Fort Houston that the settlers lived on friendly terms with the Cherokees. The stockade of unsquared logs and heavily shuttered windows hadn't been used as a fort in nineteen years. Major Houston's widow would be safe enough on the branch of Baker's Creek. Was it really rich land? James Houston considered John's eager question, then slowly shook his head. It would do, said the builder of Fort Houston, while they looked around for a better site.

His mother said nothing at all, but Sam was sure he understood the gleam in her gray eyes. They had traveled this far to reach Major Houston's chosen home, and they would live on it.

They would stay with relatives until a house was raised. James Houston decided that, and Sam's mother offered no protest. It was all right to let kinfolk get them started. Her own blood cousin walked over from the next settlement to help. Other Virginia families had put down new roots in Tennessee; new but friendly faces appeared every day. Sam felt cheated. The surroundings were new but little else was changed. The house rose to two stories—of hewn logs, yes, but clapboarded on the inside. And day and night the burning went on, as timber dwindled to fresh-scarred stumps and then into gray ashes. The Widow Houston's eldest sons were workers, no mistake about that. No flies on Mary or Isabelle, either; they took rain water and borrowed corn and made tasty, wholesome hominy and enough lye soap to last any family a year. William and Eliza Ann were small, but they gathered grass for the clay chimney and foraged for nuts and berries as if their young lives were at stake. The only loafer was Sam, who was hefty enough to shoulder a log instead of snaking it down the hillside. Ask at the spreading clearing where he was and a brother grunted "Off somewhere," and that was all to be learned.

Oh, he was an odd one, all right. Many young frontier bucks shied away from a walking stock and took to the timber. They grew into hunters and trappers and trail finders, and earned a grudging respect despite their fiddle-footed ways. But Sam was no great shakes at hunting and didn't cure a wild pelt that winter. His father's cousins tried to reason with him, but the Reverend Samuel Houston's was the only adult voice he heeded.

His mother knew what this strange son of hers was, and urged patience. Sam, she felt, had inherited many of his father's traits along with the name. Major Houston had never found his niche in life; a militia leader performed irregular service. Elizabeth Houston defended her son in one breath and prayed for him in the next. God, she was sure, would watch over him.

Other eyes watched him, too—dark beady eyes. Sam finally realized that someone was trailing after him. It frightened him a little, but he set a trap for his pursuer. He made a loop of wild grapevine and sent a boulder rolling down a hillside. Here came his stalker at a quick run. Sam jerked the vine with perfect timing and the slim Indian youth pitched forward on his face.

Sam helped his quarry rise. Now it was the Indian's turn to be uneasy.

"How?" Sam said in his friendliest manner. But the Cherokee youth wasn't reassured. He grunted and took to his heels. Sam followed a short distance and then gave up the chase.

The experience puzzled him. He hadn't felt the slightest fear of the Indian; nor enmity, either. He had set his trap more from curiosity than anything else. And he had let his prize escape before learning anything about him.

He was sure the Reverend Mr. Houston could help him.

"He was a Cherokee," the scholarly frontiersman said after hearing Sam's description. "They wear cotton garments. Raise their own cotton, too. Most of our people see no difference between one Indian and another. But there is. The Cherokees rear their young carefully. I've visited in their villages and enjoyed it."

Sam trudged slowly homeward, musing over his relative's words. He must learn about the Cherokees, he decided; learn for himself the difference between one clan and the next.

"I saw a Cherokee today," he told his family at supper.

"What was the varmint doing?" John asked quickly. "Not skulking around our livestock, was he?"

John was as proud of their sleek Holstein cows as of the newly cleared fields. Now their worry was whether or not the hillsides would yield enough corn to fatten their stock.

Sam frowned. The Indian he had seen was no "varmint"; nor was he bent on thievery, either.

"Keep a lookout for 'em," said Paxton. "Maybe we can depend on you for that much, anyhow."

Sam finished his meal in silence. Later, by candlelight, he reread several favorite passages from the *Iliad.* His mother finally brought him the family Bible.

"If you're going to put your eyes out reading," she said, "spend more time with this. It'll do you more good than these yarns about ancient Greeks."

Sam wanted to answer that the Bible concerned ancient people, too, but didn't. His mother tolerated no sort of lightness about either the Good Book or her church's Sunday services. Sam wasn't thinking of levity anyhow. The Bible was a great, stirring book indeed, especially the Old Testament. He could recite long passages from the Song of Solomon. The Reverend Mr. Houston urged reverent study of the Bible, too. Once you've learned the Bible and the *Iliad* by heart, claimed Cousin Samuel, you are an educated man. You have the mind to grasp and master every situation.

Did he? Sam Houston searched his conscience as he roamed farther into the woods. He felt no guilt because of his poor contribution to the family effort. Neither his mother nor his brothers needed him. No more self-sufficient family had ever taken roots in the Smokies. Was Sam shiftless and no-good because he disliked scratching in the hillsides or herding placid Holsteins? He had to know; he owed it to himself to find out. And he couldn't learn the answer at home. The woods might offer no solution either. Where else could he look?

Next time the Indian caught him unawares. Sam was sound asleep beside a shallow, swift creek. The Cherokee shook him awake and proudly showed two golden-scaled mountain perch.

"We eat," the Indian said.

Sam sat up quickly. "You talk *English!*"

The Cherokee smiled. "My father part white. My name John Rogers." He hesitated, then added, "We belong to the Jolly clan. Our chief is Oo-loo-te-ka."

"Oo-loo-te-ka!" Sam repeated. The musical sound fascinated him. So did his new acquaintance's accent.

"He-Puts-the-Drum-Away," John Rogers translated.

"Oh," said Sam. The name must mean that this Cherokee's father wanted peace with the whites. "Where is your camp?"

John gestured to the east. "On an island in the river. But no camp. We live there long time." He started a fire with two stones. "My father head man to John Jolly," he added proudly. "And Oo-loo-te-ka sits in the Cherokee Grand Council."

"What's that?"

"White man know little of Cherokees," John said disgustedly. "Cherokee council older than theirs."

Sam nodded. He knew nothing at all, but he was willing to learn.

His newly acquired knowledge thrilled him as he started home with the setting sun. So the Cherokee village in the Tennessee River was part of a great nation, with actually a capital and a council like the United States Congress! And the Cherokees weren't nomadic hunters, but pastoral people living in attached houses and raising corn and vegetables and tending cattle. But not like white men—John Rogers quickly explained the difference. Indian families didn't drive themselves to own the biggest cribs or the most cows. Why raise more than they intended to eat themselves?

"You needn't worry about Cherokees stealing our cattle," Sam told his brothers that night. "They're as well off as we are."

Maybe better, he thought, comparing John Rogers' happy, friendly expression with the tired, grim faces of his brothers.

"How do you know so much?" James demanded.

Sam explained. His family's reaction stunned him. His mother and brothers heard him out. Then John turned to Mrs. Houston.

"Well, what do you think now?"

Tears showed faintly in her eyes. "We can't have him traipsing around in the woods with Indians," she conceded. "I suppose the store is the only thing."

Sam looked at her blankly. What store? He had heard nothing before of his mother's plan to buy part interest in a Maryville store, but he was told now. The family had several hundred dollars left. Mr. Tim Montgomery's health was failing. He needed help in the store as well as more capital. James wanted to learn the merchant's trade; farming didn't suit him either, though he had worked diligently that winter. Mr. Montgomery was willing to train two Houston boys. Since Sam "took" to nothing else, he must try his hand as a store clerk. John and James put it more coldly than his mother. There must be *something* Sam was good for.

He agreed without enthusiasm. He couldn't deny that he was too near grown for idleness. At fifteen he stood six feet two inches and weighed over a hundred and eighty pounds. It seemed a pity to waste such strength behind a store counter, but what else was there? Certainly Sam admitted that he wasn't cut out to till fields.

But one thing rankled him. He was going into Mr. Montgomery's store as some sort of punishment. Why? For being friendly with the son of a Cherokee head man? For absorbing all he could learn in one day about the Cherokee civilization? If that was his immediate offense, then Sam couldn't accept the discipline in good spirit—for his curiosity wasn't satisfied. He wanted to learn more not only about the Cherokees but about all people—why and how they organized their governments, even Indians, and why some governments succeeded and others failed. Sam doubted if he would learn much about those things behind a dry-goods counter.

★ 2

The Prodigal Returns

JAMES AND JOHN WERE SAM'S LEGAL GUARDIANS. MAJOR Houston's will had made that quite clear. His wife and two older sons were executors and guardians of the other children until their twenty-first birthdays. The will further recommended that the "younger sons be put to such trade as may seem beneficial."

So Sam could be put behind a dry-goods counter and told to "learn the business." But keeping him there was something else. He worked fairly diligently through the autumn and winter months. To all appearances he was "settled."

Then came spring, and Sam became restless. He hadn't come to the frontier to measure cloth by the yard and fret over small profits. This was no promised destiny, but only sheer existence. He struggled with a hundred assorted schemes as he dutifully waited on Mr. Montgomery's customers. None of them formed into anything definite. Finally, acting on sudden impulse, he slipped out of the store and melted into the woods. He intended only to seize a deserved holiday.

He saw small chance of meeting the Cherokee youth again. Nor was he seeking out John Rogers in particular. He meant only to wander awhile and dream.

But the young Cherokee came noiselessly through the timber and greeted Sam warmly. Short acquaintance speedily formed into friendship and boyhood rivalry. John issued the first challenge. Sam's eyes gleamed. This slender strippling wanted to wrestle!

Sam nodded as John explained how Cherokees matched strength. They stretched out side by side and intertwined touching legs. The idea was to flip the other over. Sam grunted and strained as John applied unexpected strength. The Cherokee feinted weakness, then caught Sam off guard. Sam floundered over on his side as John chortled in triumph.

"You beat me," conceded Sam. "But let's try it again. You won't fool me this time."

But John did. The Cherokee won several such bouts before Sam managed to win a single one.

"You wear me out," said John, panting a little. "You are determined to triumph."

Sam smiled. So he was. It was a small thing, he mused. He was the stronger and had the longer legs. His thrill came not from winning but from learning.

The sun was already low over the timber-clad mountains. "I must go," John said regretfully. He hesitated. "Come with me?" he asked. "You will be welcome in my father's lodge."

Sam took a deep breath. He wanted to go with the Indian lad; he wanted to desperately. His respite from Mr. Montgomery's discipline had only whetted his appetite. Besides, he dreaded the punishment in store for him. Mr. Montgomery might even whip him.

"I will go with you," Sam suddenly decided. His mother would be worried; he brooded about that as he followed John through the timber. But he couldn't turn back now. He couldn't stifle his curiosity. He must learn for himself how these coppery people lived in such happiness and dignity in these mountains.

John chattered as they trotted along, Sam listening closely, nodding several times. When he stood face to face with John Jolly, Chief Oo-loo-te-ka, he didn't forget the instructions John had given him.

"I come," Sam said quietly.

Jolly's wrinkled face glowed approval. "You do," he answered gravely. Oo-loo-te-ka was pleased to meet a white youth so respectful of his elders.

Chief Jolly's village occupied an island in the Tennessee River. Sam's curious eyes weren't idle a minute even as he acknowledged John's proud introductions to old and young. These were no savages, but proud, gentle people. They lived comfortably, in sturdy attached lodges. They ate well; John's beaming mother set out a savory stew and Sam ate ravenously. It was a *burgoo,* he learned. He wolfed down bites of venison and fish highly seasoned with wild herbs.

They ate, then played. Sam was the center of eager attention from John's brothers and sisters. How fast could he run? Had he really bested John in wrestling? A slim girl called Tiana mocked his efforts to seize her in a Cherokee version of tag. Sam ran until he was completely exhausted. He slept wrapped in a deerskin robe. Never, he mused, had he known such an exciting day.

John shook him awake at daybreak. The younger Cherokees were practicing their ball play. A nearby village had challenged John Jolly's people. The clan's honor was at stake.

Sam confessed his ignorance of any sort of ball games.

"Watch us awhile," said John. "You can learn."

Sam watched closely. He saw that the game required speed, endurance and strength. The ball was round, hollow and light. The Indians batted it back and forth with a stick until a score was made.

Sam quickly formed his own ideas about how the game should be played. Most of the players, it seemed to him, dashed about too recklessly. Each tried to take responsibility for the whole playing area. It impressed the tall novice at the game as foolish to pursue the ball everywhere.

The practice halted at noon. Ball play was a full-day contest. The youths ate and rested briefly and then were ready for a fresh start.

"Let me try," Sam asked John. The chief's son readily agreed. He voiced some instructions as Sam took a defensive position.

Then the ball was flying around and John forgot about his white visitor—until, that is, Sam intercepted a solid hit and propelled the ball from danger. Then John let out a happy whoop. There was no longer any doubt about Sam's ability. He waved and shouted instructions to his teammates. Quickly Sam supplanted John as the leader of one team.

Sam's size made a big difference. He had greater reach and could hit harder, but he believed his big advantage was his cool attitude. He wasted no energy. He anticipated the opposition's moves.

They played until near dark. John made the proposal as they ate. Sam must play with them against the clan of Tah-ehon-tusky.

Sam shook his head. Already he had been gone a day and night. What was his mother thinking, and his brothers? His lips tightened. He could well imagine what Mr. Montgomery was saying. The storekeeper had been dubious of his services in the first place. He had asked Elizabeth Houston for one of the other sons—James or

William, anyone but Sam. "I got the cull of the bunch," Mr. Montgomery had told his customers in Sam's hearing.

Now he knew he must return and endure his punishment.

"You can't go," insisted John. "Let me see if I can make you understand," and he told Sam the history of Cherokee ball play. It was a lyrical account, almost a song. The birds, led by the eagle, challenged the beasts, led by the bear. The birds had triumphed, mainly because of the bat and the flying squirrel. At first the heroes had been rejected by the haughty eagle. They were such ignoble birds, not worthy to be in his ranks. Sam's lips twitched. It was an appealing tale, especially as John narrated it. Sam was reminded of the *Iliad*.

He sighed. He knew what his brothers would say. So much fuss over a silly ball game! But he sensed the feeling of these new dusky friends. The honor of Oo-loo-te-ka's village was no small thing, even in ball play.

"I'll play," Sam decided. He was needed here and appreciated here. The punishment for his holiday would be no greater a week hence.

Oo-loo-te-ka's clan won a close, thrilling victory. That night the Cherokees gave their new hero a name, Co-lon-neh, the Raven—the name revered in Cherokee story and song. The first raven had been scorched badly while bringing fire to save mankind. Hence the raven's jet blackness, and his honored place in Cherokee tradition.

The next day Sam trudged slowly homeward. He was not surprised to find that Mr. Montgomery refused to reinstate him as an apprentice. Nor did Sam suffer any great remorse. He did not want to learn such a trade anyway; what he had learned from his stay with the Cherokees seemed much more important.

His mother and brothers conferred again. What could be done with such a young man! Would he try to prepare himself as a schoolmaster? Sam sat dutifully through two academy terms. Greek fascinated him and he earned quick acclaim in rhetoric. Upon his return to Maryville he opened a private school. It flourished for a time—until the young schoolmaster shut its doors and returned to his Indian friends.

Months later a canoe touched sand on the Cherokee island and the two older Houston sons splashed ashore. John and James came first to plead, but prepared also to threaten. They weren't willing to abandon their brother to the Cherokees. But if Sam was obdurate, he must relinquish his share of the growing Houston estate.

"You could open your school again," John argued. "Hang it, Sam, you proved you could amount to something. If you'd just try—"

Sam shook his head. He never intended to open another school. The determined brothers brought up another point—Sam's personal debts. He had spent his meager earnings and more, mostly on presents for his Cherokee friends.

"Those debts must be paid, Sam," James said sternly. "We have the family honor to think about. If you won't pay them, we will."

Honor! James Houston had spoken a magic word. The Raven lived on, jet black but honored. Sam stirred. Of course his honor must be protected.

"You owe over a hundred dollars, Sam," John pointed out.

Sam nodded glumly. He must be an unworthy Houston indeed—as the Maryville community measured a man. The Cherokees believed differently, of course. They admired Co-lon-neh for his strength, his intellect and his personal charm. Sam sighed. He knew he possessed those qualities. He knew, too, that the Indians had helped him develop them. It wasn't enough to impress the Cherokees. He must earn recognition in the greater world surrounding the island, the white man's world. He was twenty years old. His days of boyhood were over. He must face the responsibilities of manhood.

"Wait for me," he told his brothers. "I'll go back with you."

John Houston's face brightened.

"I must say farewell to John Jolly."

The older brothers returned to the canoe to wait. Sam moved deliberately. This wouldn't be easy to do. He had loved these coppery people and was loved in return, but he must leave them now. They would understand why. They understood duty and honor better than most white men.

He stood before Oo-loo-te-ka.

"I go," he said simply, pointing to his brothers.

The chief's lips twitched but he showed no other expression. The gleam in his eyes could mean anything—sorrow, pity or pride.

"You do," Oo-loo-te-ka said simply.

The war was just now affecting the West. It had broken out as a sea fight between the United States and Great Britain; then hostilities opened on the Canadian border. By 1813 the conflict engulfed Tennessee and the other southern states. No English invasion was feared, but British agents aroused Indians to ravage white settlements. Tecumseh, the Shawnee prophet, stirred the Creeks to declare full-scale war.

Militia regiments tried to subdue the Indians and failed miserably. The Creeks were more formidable than white men first realized. Sam knew of their fighting prowess; the Cherokees considered the Creek Nation the most warlike of the southern clans. Oo-loo-te-ka's council had been considering an alliance with the white men before Sam returned to Maryville and Porter Academy.

He found it easy to hold aloof from the first wave of excitement. He wondered if his prejudice against militia could be traced back to his father. Probably so, for Major Houston had struggled all his life with the frustrations of such volunteers.

Then the United States Army announced organization of a regular division, appointed Andrew Jackson to its command and sent recruiting parties into the East Tennessee settlements.

The regulars reached Maryville on March 24, 1813. They marched in spick-and-span, wearing white pantaloons and waistcoats, bearing smoothbore muskets. Drums rolled, the colors were presented, and the sergeant voiced an eloquent appeal for volunteers. He dropped shining silver dollars on the drumhead as tokens.

Sam's eyes gleamed in sudden decision. He stepped forward dramatically and picked up a silver dollar.

The sergeant beamed. "Now we're getting somewhere," he shouted. "Let's have a dozen more as big as this one—if there's any more around here his size."

Sam smiled. There weren't. Even in moccasins he stood taller than any twenty-year-old in East Tennessee.

The sergeant took no chances on losing his recruit. A private hurried off for Mrs. Elizabeth Houston. Then

John and James signed the enlistment papers, too. Their legal guardianship had another year to go. Neither brother hesitated. Certainly one member of the Houston clan should answer the call to arms. They were happy that Sam had responded on his own initiative.

Sam stood by the recruiting sergeant while the necessary formalities were completed. Quite a group gathered to watch the swearing in.

"So you're going after Injuns, Sam?" called out a spectator. "Ain't that fighting your own kind?"

Sam ignored the taunt.

"You'd better jine the militia, Sam," said another skeptical onlooker. "They make you git up and go in the regular army."

"Pay 'em no mind, son," the recruiting sergeant said anxiously.

A cold smile came to Sam's face. "They will hear of me," he declared.

His voice carried to the hecklers. "Sure," one cried. "You'll send for your brothers to git you out of this mess, too."

Sam's lips tightened. He turned and strode home.

His mother was waiting for him with a plain gold ring —a talisman for the young soldier about to face the world. On it was engraved a single word—"honor."

★ 3

Don't Count a Hero Out until He Is Dead

THE CAPTAIN WAS DISGUSTED. "YOU CALL YOURSELVES soldiers!" he stormed. "You're clumsy backwoodsmen, pea pickers. Were you all born with two left feet?"

Sam listened patiently to the tirade. The officer's wrath wasn't directed at him. He was a drill sergeant already, after only thirty days, but other recruits of the Thirty-ninth Regular Infantry were lagging behind.

"You'll be in action in two weeks!" despaired the captain. "Get that into your thick heads. You're going to the front, ready or not. Listen to me. Get these commands straight. It's the difference between living and dying." The officer heaved a deep sigh. "Now let's start over again."

Sam's detail drilled better than the others. The harassed captain made mental note of that fact. "I'll be doggoned," he said to his major, "if young Houston isn't our best drill sergeant. And he hasn't had the rank a week."

"Then we'll recommend him for ensign," decided the major. Officer material was scant. These volunteers were crack shots but slow to grasp fundamental tactics. Sam was a full-fledged ensign by February, when the Thirty-ninth reported to General Andrew Jackson at Fort Strother.

Jackson had found it difficult to hold this post in northern Alabama. The Creeks boasted a brilliant leader, Bill Weathersford. Tecumseh, a major general in the British Army, supplied powder, lead and muskets as well as fiery inspiration. The Creeks had baffled Jackson's twenty-five hundred militiamen at every turn. Five thousand more militia were coming, but Jackson placed his hopes on the regulars.

"Old Hickory" reviewed them immediately. Ensign Houston stood straight and proud but secretly awed. Andy Jackson was the ideal of every young Tennesseean. He had risen out of poverty to earn financial, political and military success. He was all kinds of a man, as Ensign Houston wanted to be.

"Houston?" General Jackson repeated slowly. A frown showed on his bony features. "From Blount County?"

"Yes, sir."

Old Hickory nodded. "I know of your people. You've done well, Ensign." His eyes suddenly softened. Usually they were like blue flints. "See that you do as well in battle."

"Yes, sir," Sam said stiffly.

The Thirty-ninth fell out to make camp. The reenforcements had marched since dawn without food or rest. Ensign Houston's men quickly pitched tents and posted guards. A young private, John Woods, asked relief from his post while he ate. Houston agreed. He saw no harm in allowing Woods to relax a few minutes.

Nor would there have been if Woods had obeyed an order by the officer of the day.

"Clean up your scraps," the lieutenant told Woods. "Were you raised in a kennel?"

Woods threatened the officer with his musket butt. Ensign Houston paled but performed his duty. He ordered Private Woods put in irons and reported the insubordination to headquarters.

Judgment came quick and harsh. Woods was missing as the Thirty-ninth marched toward the Creek entrenchment on the Horseshoe Bend of the Tallapoosa River. Happily Sam had not been required to witness the execution.

The men of the Thirty-ninth muttered about the harsh verdict. "No call to shoot a man," complained a lanky private. "He shot off his mouth, sure. But they could have drummed him out. They didn't have to shoot him."

Ensign Houston shook his head. "That's the usual penalty for insubordination," he said sternly. "Woods was shot as an example. I hope the rest of you remember this is war, not the parade ground."

They had camped on a hillside near a flowing spring. Sam roasted his dry beef on a green stick and ate Indian-fashion, supplementing the meat with charred roots, a trick he had learned from the Cherokees. A fellow trooper gingerly sampled the roots and agreed they were more wholesome than cold corn bread.

Enlisted men had the right to address officers informally around such a campfire. "You talk about war," a weather-beaten private said slyly, "as if you knew all about it. You ever tasted powder, Ensign?"

Sam confirmed that he hadn't. "I've never fired a gun at a human target," he added slowly. "You'll be led into battle by an unseasoned ensign." His eyes swept their faces. "But don't let that worry you," he said calmly. "Just follow me—that will be your only concern."

Bold words indeed for a young man with no battle experience, but Samuel Houston meant them. He caressed the heavy ring on his finger, the one his mother had slipped into his hand the night before he left. He wanted the ring to be his talisman, its inscription his life creed.

The Thirty-ninth resumed the march at daylight and near noon reached the camp of Jackson's Indian scouts. Sam almost forgot himself as he embraced John Rogers. He had known that Cherokee allies were ahead of the army, scouting the Creek fortification, but he hadn't hoped to be reunited with his Indian brother.

"You are a chief," John Rogers said proudly. The gleam in his dark eyes repaid Sam for the hard hours of drill.

The Thirty-ninth and the Cherokee scouts marched on together. That night Ensign Houston ate his rations in the Indian camp. The grumbling of his men reached Major Lemuel Montgomery. Sam was summoned promptly and lectured on his conduct.

"You have my personal sympathies," Montgomery said after Sam's efforts at explanation. "The Cherokees are invaluable allies. General Jackson has assigned them a responsible position. They're to swim the river and destroy the Creek canoes. We want no retreat, and the Cherokees will make sure Weathersford doesn't get away."

"Yes, sir," Sam agreed. "We can depend on that."

"But you must hold the respect of your men," the major warned him. "They resent a white man who is so friendly with Indians. It doesn't matter to them that the Cherokees are our allies."

"It matters to me," Sam said stiffly. "I want the respect of my platoon. But I also treasure my Cherokee friends."

"Very well, Houston," the major said a bit disgustedly. This tall ensign, he mused, was either an unusual man or a headstrong young fool. Time must decide which.

The Cherokee scouts had slipped close enough to learn the pattern of the Creek fortifications. The small peninsula was protected on three sides by the swift Tallapoosa River. A stout barricade of green logs and packed earth blocked the approach by land. Weathersford commanded three thousand well-armed warriors, who had been provided with British muskets and powder by Tecumseh.

When his troops were in position, General Jackson trained his cannon on the log embankment. Heavy shot tore through the treetops and crashed against the barricade. The Creeks shouted back taunts. Their dialect was akin to the Cherokee tongue; Ensign Houston understood their boasts as he led his platoon forward. The Creeks claimed no damage from the bombardment. Let the white devils waste their shot and powder.

Sam stationed his men according to battle plan. He held them motionless even though musket fire sounded in the woods nearby. Had Jackson issued orders to fire? If so, Ensign Houston hadn't received them. He managed to keep his impatient men quiet. No shooting yet. No lead wasted on the coppery targets showing briefly on the parapet. "Hold your fire, men." The ensign pretended calmness.

A commotion broke out a few paces from him. Sam hurried toward the sound. Two of his soldiers had wrestled a half-naked Indian into submission. This was a Cherokee runner, a warrior without headdress or ornament of any sort. His features brightened as Sam questioned him in the Cherokee tongue. As the Indian talked in swift gutturals, Sam listened in amazement. Then he chose two privates to escort the Cherokee to General Jackson.

"What in tarnation was that about?" demanded Will Pickett.

Sam couldn't resist an explanation. Pickett was one of those who had criticized his young officer for fraternizing with Indians.

"The Cherokees spotted the Creek war canoes," he explained. "They swam the river and destroyed Weathersford's boats. On their own, too. We have the Creeks bottled up. If we do our duty, this will be their last stand."

"By gum," muttered Pickett, "you got to hand it to those Cherokees." He relayed word of this development. "Now we got to get them," he avowed. "We can't let a bunch of Cherokees show us up."

The order to charge didn't come. A white flag showed in the Creek parapet, but Weathersford had no intention of surrendering. Explanations swept through the thick timber. The Creeks had learned their retreat was cut off and asked a respite to move their women and children out of danger. General Jackson agreed.

Grumbling swept the ranks. Why not wipe out the whole red caboodle while they were about it? But officers as determined as Ensign Houston kept the recalcitrants in line.

Sam, whittling a canoe out of cedar, set a pattern of coolness for his followers, but actually he was as tense as any man in the Thirty-ninth. Tenser, perhaps; he felt he had more to lose.

Screaming came again from the Creek entrenchment. Now only warriors faced the white men's advance.

Drums rolled behind the Thirty-ninth. Sam gestured to his platoon to await orders; then the order came from Major Lemuel Montgomery. Sam raced forward, his long legs churning. He meant to be the first man over the barricade, but he wasn't. Montgomery had too much of a lead. The major vaulted to the top while Sam was grasping for a hold. But Montgomery never made it; he was killed at once. However, Sam managed to strike the first blow inside the entrenchment. His sword swung relentlessly at the enemy, and several Creek warriors fell. Then a searing pain hit Sam, staggering him, as a Creek arrow embedded itself deep in his thigh.

He couldn't stop and he mustn't fall, he told himself. The Thirty-ninth was storming the barricade in full force. It was a close hand-to-hand combat, and the Creeks were wavering.

Sam managed to support himself against a nearby tree. He pulled hard at the barb but he couldn't move it. He caught Lieutenant James Pierce by the shoulder and ordered him to yank out the arrow! Pierce shook his head and shuddered. "I'll help you to the rear, Ensign. You need a surgeon."

Sam refused, so Pierce seized the shaft and pulled. The arrow remained firmly implanted in his flesh.

"Pull, man," groaned Sam. "I can stand the pain."

He was out of his mind with searing pain and disappointed fury. He must press on, regain control of his platoon. The Creeks were falling around him. The greatest Indian battle in the South's long history was approaching its climax. This was no time for an ambitious ensign to limp toward the rear.

Out came the arrow after another tremendous tug, blood gushing from the wound. Everything seemed crimson before Sam's eyes. He felt himself falling, sinking into this churning, bottomless sea. He fought against it, flailing out with both hands. He was sure he was swimming against a relentless tide, but he wasn't. He was crawling instead, egged on by his instinct for self-preservation. Inching back over a barricade, he fell forward and downward.

He heard voices around him, felt someone shaking his shoulder. He blinked away the red torrent, and looked up into the bony features of General Jackson.

"Are you all right, Ensign?"

"Yes, sir," Sam said hoarsely. He struggled to his feet, and Jackson hurried off. The Creeks had split ranks and taken to the thick undergrowth. Some broke away from the hot pursuit to make another stand.

Sam snatched up a musket and limped back to his platoon, which was milling uncertainly around. Should they wait for further orders or push ahead? Sam refused to delay. He hobbled straight ahead, a weaving, eerie shape. The Thirty-ninth re-formed and came up behind him. A sudden volley sent Sam spinning. One ball shattered his right arm. Another smashed his shoulder. He tottered to within a step of the redoubt, then pitched forward on his face.

The battle was over for Ensign Houston.

For the Creeks, too. The white men turned an Indian stratagem against the fearless warriors. Fire arrows drove the Creeks out of their last stronghold. They perished by the hundreds. Red men would never fight another major battle east of the Mississippi River.

★ 4

The West "Takes" Washington

RECOVERY CAME SLOWLY. ELIZABETH HOUSTON COULD keep her son alive, but full healing required technical skills. The army's field surgeons had not tried to take the bullet out of Sam's smashed shoulder. He was too weak for such an operation when he was brought out of the Alabama wilderness on a litter. He was sent home to convalesce, if he could.

His mother engaged a Knoxville physician to aid Sam's recovery, and, to that worthy gentleman's astonishment, the patient rapidly regained strength. Two months later Sam was able to travel about and enjoy his leave. Before rejoining his regiment, he visited Washington. There he saw the ashes of the Capitol and the President's home, both burned by British invaders. The sight made him eager for action again. Against his doctor's advice he returned to duty, but too late to fight the British. He found his comrades in arms celebrating the victory of New Orleans. There the Tennesseeans had found English regulars less formidable than Weathersford's Creeks.

Second Lieutenant Sam Houston! His promotion came

early in 1815, also an assignment to New Orleans with the First Infantry.

It was a gay duty, until the damp climate aggravated Sam's wounded shoulder. Army doctors decided the bullet must be removed at any cost. The ball came out, but Sam carried the shoulder stiffly the rest of his days.

Peacetime assignment was boring. By 1817 Sam Houston was eager for a transfer. His request came to the attention of General Jackson, who remembered the proud young ensign of Fort Strother. He remembered, too, that Houston was well regarded by the Cherokees.

The general had need of such a man. He was planning the destruction of another Indian foe, the Seminoles. But such a campaign must be postponed until the Cherokees were moved west of the Mississippi.

He sent for Lieutenant Houston and explained his purpose.

Sam shook his head. He knew of the treaty of 1816, by which some Cherokee chieftains had traded 1,300,000 acres of their homelands for even larger tracts in the West. But other chiefs refused to leave East Tennessee. Their cornfields were there; their gods dwelt in those skies. Sam explained the Cherokee prejudice against the West. That was the direction of the darkening sky; it meant death.

Andrew Jackson scowled. He was not accustomed to young officers who rejected his ideas. An unusual young man indeed, he decided, studying Sam more closely.

"Must we destroy them?" demanded the general. "Must they be slaughtered as were the Creeks? The treaty was signed. White settlers are impatient for the lands to be offered for public use. My next order from Washington will be to move against the Cherokees. Do you want that?"

"No," Sam said at once. The Creeks had been destroyed despite their alliance with England and their fine new weapons. The Cherokees would stand no chance in war against the white man.

"You can perform a valuable service," Jackson went on. "If you will apply for assignment to the Cherokees, I will use what influence I have in your behalf. You have proved yourself a good soldier. Now you can serve your state and country in a more vital way. It is better to avoid war than to win a battle."

Sam studied Jackson's proposal. The prospect held no appeal for him; but the more he brooded, the surer he became that he must face this unpleasant duty. There must be no bloodshed between United States Regulars and Oo-loo-te-ka's people. The lieutenant sent his application to Washington. His appointment was announced almost immediately. Obviously Andrew Jackson could get what he wanted in Washington.

Sam discarded army regalia for beaded buckskins. Oo-loo-te-ka greeted Co-lon-neh warmly but shook his head as Sam explained his mission. The Cherokees would not accept removal beyond the Mississippi.

Sam had talked straight to his new superiors. If he were to deal with the Cherokees, then he must know that his promises would be kept. He meant to spare Jolly's clan from the "Trail of Tears," as the exodus of the other Cherokee clans had come to be known. Many of them had died en route to the West; all had suffered.

"You will go as people of honor," Sam promised. "You will not be herded like cattle. You will not be mistreated by white guards. Your people will not starve." He sighed. "It is not my will that you go, my Father. Nor will I bear arms against you if war comes. I will not shed Cherokee blood. But I cannot stop it. I can only require that the conditions of any agreement be met."

In solemn council Oo-loo-te-ka and his chiefs decided against a futile war. John Jolly placed his people at the mercy of his white protégé.

Sam saw that the Cherokees were treated well. Jolly's clan of three hundred and forty-one men, women and children traveled to their new lands on well-provisioned flatboats. Each warrior boasted a gleaming new rifle.

Other reluctant Cherokee clans followed suit. Sam Houston won promotion to first lieutenant and the official praise of Tennessee's governor. More important, Sam realized his potentials as a mediator, a counselor. When he voiced his new ambition to General Jackson, Old Hickory gave full encouragement. "By all means," agreed the general. "Resign your commission and qualify yourself to practice law. Gain admission to the bar," promised Jackson, "and you will hear from me again."

But Sam needed more than encouragement. He must have financial help. Again he was in debt. His pay as second lieutenant had failed to meet his expenses.

He bought a horse and rode back to Maryville. How would his brothers respond to this new appeal? They had done much to help him already. He had been a problem since his fifteenth year.

His reception quickly removed any doubts. John and James greeted him proudly, as did Robert. All agreed that Sam could be successful as a lawyer.

"You will need money," James mused. "The crops have been only tolerable. But I reckon—"

Sam shook his head. He wanted no loan. With Paxton and Isabelle dead, he owned one-eighth interest in the family estate, and this he sold to his brothers. Now only sentimental ties bound him to the East Tennessee mountains. Now he was really on his own.

Eight months later an impressive carriage stopped outside the post office of Lebanon, in central Tennessee. The building was a plain frame structure, just as the postmaster, Isaac Galladay, was a plain sort of man. Mr. Galladay greeted his visitor cordially. Who didn't recognize Billy Carroll, Old Hickory's personal spokesman in all political matters? Talk was that Carroll would be Tennessee's next governor.

"You have a young lawyer lodging with you—Sam Houston?"

Carroll got to the question quickly. Plainly, his main business in Lebanon was to learn all he could about Attorney Houston.

"Sure do," nodded Galladay. "I've sort of helped him along. He's a go-getter."

Carroll nodded. "I must see him. I'm sure we have something to discuss."

Galladay sent a messenger for Sam. Houston was walking along a country lane, struggling with his own impatiences. He couldn't understand his scarcity of clients. He had accomplished a near miracle, passing his bar examination after only six months of study. Fate had guided him to Postmaster Galladay, who had rented him a small office for one dollar a month. Furthermore Mr. Galladay had guaranteed Sam's credit. The fledgling lawyer had bought a wardrobe befitting any Nashville dandy—bell-crowned beaver, plum-colored coat, tight breeches and colorful waistcoats. No Lebanon social gathering was complete without Sam, and men listened respectfully to his opinions on public matters. He had acquired maturity and dignity, but he hadn't acquired the one trait he admired in his brothers—the ability to earn money and to keep it.

Galladay's messenger interrupted his bitter thoughts, and he hurried back to the post office. He and Billy Carroll sat on a wooden bench behind Sam's office, and Sam whittled as Carroll talked.

The man was convincing. One had only to listen a few minutes to realize Carroll was no average politician. The combination of Andy Jackson and Billy was invincible in Tennessee. Which was the stronger? Sam had always believed Old Hickory did the planning and Carroll ran the errands. Now he wasn't so sure.

"Tennessee needs young men," Billy Carroll said. "The creation of every new county calls for regularly elected officials—judges, prosecuting attorneys, members of the legislature. These places should go to young men who are capable of going further. Tennessee is rising to leadership west of the Alleghenies. And the West must become dominant on the national scene."

Sam's jackknife kept going as Carroll talked; his thoughts were as busy. To what was Carroll leading? If Andy Jackson wanted him as a political lieutenant, why didn't he say so? It could be that simple. Then Sam recalled the rumor that Jackson and Carroll had reached a clear-cut division of influence. Jackson guided the "machine" as far as national politics was concerned. Carroll called the turns in Tennessee affairs.

"This district," Carroll said, "will elect a prosecuting attorney this summer. You are inexperienced in courtrooms. But you are loyal and ambitious. If you should get elected, and serve a creditable term—"

Sam shut the jackknife. He was ready to promise both.

"Then," continued Billy Carroll, "we would think

about Washington in 1823. I won't deny that Mr. Jackson has some important plans for the following year."

Sam closed his eyes. His lips moved soundlessly. Carroll's blessing amounted to election as prosecuting attorney. Then Jackson's endorsement would be all any presentable candidate needed to win a seat in the House of Representatives. The Jackson–Carroll combine was writing a new chapter in American politics.

Sam chose his words carefully. He was eager for a fling in politics. He welcomed the sponsorship of both Carroll and Jackson. Any young man would.

"But," he added, "if I can make myself understood—at the risk of seeming presumptuous I must make it clear, sir, that Houston always votes his own dictates, and his own conscience."

Billy Carroll smiled to himself. Most young men, he knew, started out with similar high ideals. High-spirited young men made the best candidates. Those who could hold their personal standards and still achieve political accomplishments made the best officeholders.

The two shook hands on their bargains. Carroll traveled on west. Towns were organizing between the Tennessee and Mississippi rivers. Carroll meant to annex these frontier settlements to the empire he and Andy Jackson had conceived.

Sam Houston, according to Carroll, was a fine political prospect. His family was prominent in East Tennessee. Sam himself was popular in the mountains for his successful arbitration with the Cherokees. He had marched and fought with Jackson, whose former soldiers dominated the western part of the state.

District attorney, then congressman—that was Carroll's recommendation for Sam Houston, and Jackson approved. Old Hickory was organizing his ranks for a presidential bid in 1824. He needed willing helpers along the Potomac.

Sam's political career advanced on schedule. He served a two-year term as district attorney and then won election to Congress in 1823. In the same year he was chosen a general of the Tennessee militia.

Washington! The towering gentleman from Tennessee attracted immediate attention. He came carefully and fashionably dressed, even to a narrow-brimmed beaver hat. He drew listeners when he spoke; the musical resonance learned from the Cherokees held unusual appeal.

Sam found lodging at the inn operated by William O'Neale. Meals were one dollar a day, costly for the times, but he considered the expense justified. The two senators from Tennessee, John W. Eaton and Jackson himself, boarded there. Other public figures spent leisure hours in Major O'Neale's tavern. Some fascinated Sam; others disgusted him.

Congressman Daniel Webster and actor Junius Booth were soon friends of the young Tennesseean. Webster was the most brilliant orator in Congress; Booth dominated the American theater. Both offered help to the political novice.

"You speak too much like an actor," scolded Webster. "Learn gravity and more dignity. This is Congress, not a stage."

"You have possibilities," Booth told Sam in private. "You dare to appear as a natural personality. But at times, sir, you sound like just another lawyer. Do not let hidebound conventions conceal your natural talents."

Sam thanked both, grateful for their attention. He spent much of his leisure time in their company, but often days passed without his seeing either. Andrew Jackson drove lieutenants as hard in politics as in war. There was little respite for a young congressman who became a more trusted aide each passing day.

Jackson's dream had seemed farfetched at first. There were two major parties, the Whigs and the Democrats. Their character had changed slightly, but essentially these were the factions formed in America's first political cleavage. The Whigs traced their development back to Alexander Hamilton. The Democrats had evolved from the strong champion of states' rights, Thomas Jefferson.

The basic difference was geographic—New England against the South. But the Whig party was taking on a new character. Henry Clay of Kentucky was gradually assuming its leadership. The union of New England and western congressmen outvoted the regular Democrats, led by John C. Calhoun.

There was Jackson's opening—the Democratic party's dire need for support in the so-called West, the states fronting along the Mississippi.

The southern bloc eagerly wooed the comparative newcomers to the Washington scene; it must. The abolitionist movement grew stronger every day. The South saw slavery as its economic foundation. Sam Houston sensed immediately that Jackson's presidential chances depended upon his attitude toward states' rights. Did a state or states have the constitutional right to secede from the Union?

Old Hickory did not flinch. He rose at an important political banquet and delivered a toast which threw the South into turmoil.

"To our Federal Union," Jackson said gravely. "It must be preserved."

Young Sam Houston applauded such a courageous stand. Mr. Calhoun did not. The South Carolina senator immediately formed a coalition against Jackson's candidacy. Better to elect a Whig, reasoned Calhoun, than a Democrat who denied the constitutional rights of individual states.

Jackson knew he had severed political links with the South. His only chance was to lure western leaders from the Whig party. He assigned that task to Sam.

Sam found Kentucky leaders willing to listen, even Henry Clay. Political unity of the West! It must come inevitably. Why not now? Was Clay convinced? Sam could not be sure.

Clay seemed receptive to the idea. Election night found Jackson hoping for victory in his first try for the presidency. Early returns showed him the choice of eleven states. John Quincy Adams, the Whig candidate, led in only six. But neither aspirant managed to win a majority in the electoral college. That put the election into the House of Representatives. The tally was close, but Kentucky's votes went to Adams.

Almost immediately Clay was appointed Secretary of State.

Sam tried to take personal blame for the defeat. "I should have learned about such a swap," he said unhappily. He was convinced that Clay had been promised the cabinet post in return for Kentucky's votes.

But Jackson refused to hold any one lieutenant responsible. "Let this defeat of 1824 be a lesson," he said coldly. "We had it coming," he reasoned. "We'll be smarter in 1828."

Sam's eyes lit up as Old Hickory explained his strategy for the next election. They must win eastern Democrats to their side. The "Jackson party" set their sights on

New York. Sam approached DeWitt Clinton, offering the vice-presidential spot on the "western ticket." Clinton refused for himself, but accepted for Martin Van Buren.

Jackson and Van Buren! Their eager campaigners left no stone unturned, and in 1828 the gaunt Tennessee general was elevated to the White House.

Eager thousands poured into Washington for Jackson's inauguration. Men in buckskin rubbed shoulders with European diplomats and eastern investors. Jackson ordered the doors of the president's mansion thrown open. Let the people from the frontier gape at the thick carpets and finger the costly drapes. The country west of the Alleghenies had come of age. A political revolution had been won. Huzzah for Old Hickory! Never had the Potomac witnessed such enthusiasm.

Sam Houston stood at Jackson's right hand to welcome the visitors from Tennessee, Ohio, Kentucky, Indiana. He was the center of much attention himself. Wasn't he Jackson's heir apparent, the trusted lieutenant who had engineered the New York coup? He was young, only thirty-five. Why doubt that he would someday follow in old Andy's footsteps?

Sam did nothing to discourage such speculation. Why should he? Jackson would serve eight years. Then the West would support a New Yorker as promised. Vice-President Van Buren would succeed Old Hickory if the new political coalition held together. But after Van Buren—why not Sam Houston?

★ 5

Brave Hearts Also Break

THE BACKDROP CHANGED. SAM HOUSTON WAS BACK IN Tennessee campaigning for governor. Billy Carroll was finishing his third term in the office. The state constitution required that he wait two years before seeking reelection, but the Jackson–Carroll coalition had no intention of losing its grip on the governor's mansion. Let young Houston fill the post for two years, then return to Washington.

Sam was willing. He had found political success on the Potomac, but not personal happiness. He still lived alone in a crowd. He fascinated young women; they clustered around him at social functions. But none regarded him as husband material. Miss Mary Curtis of Virginia had left him hurt and troubled. She had encouraged him some, then suddenly announced her betrothal to a young man just out of West Point, Robert E. Lee.

Sam welcomed a new hunting ground. He wasn't bothered by taunts that he was a "runner" for Andy Jackson.

"My firm and undeviating attachment to General Jackson," he declared, "has brought me all the enemies I have. And I glory in the firmness of my attachment."

Both Old Hickory and Carroll advised milder speeches. Sam went his own way. He could connive and wangle for another man—Jackson especially—but not for himself. He could only stand erect and bare his chest to assaults.

He traveled Tennessee from the Smokies to the thick-timbered bottoms of the Hatchie River and the bustling bluffs of Mississippi. He wore a bell-crowned black hat, ruffled shirt, black satin vest and gleaming black wide-bottomed trousers. He drew every eye at a reception given by Colonel John Allen of Gallatin. In turn, Eliza Allen attracted his full attention.

Sam remembered her as a skinny, small child with unusually large eyes and long strands of rebellious hair. But here she stood, a well-poised young woman embarrassed by the intentness of his stare.

"I am deeply sorry," he apologized. "You have taken my breath away."

He turned to his host. "Can I help it, Colonel? The fault is yours. You should have given me warning. What right have you to so suddenly thrust me before this vision!"

Did a man just glance at a maid and decide he must wed her? Apparently so. Sam rode on to another town next day, and back to Gallatin went the first love letter of his life. The Cherokees had taught him flowing speech but not formal composition.

"I am confident of winning the governorship," he informed the dazed Allen. "But I greatly fear that in pursuing that fleece I have lost my heart."

Another missive for Eliza arrived two days later. "You will shortly hear that I have fought a duel. I may die in it. I want you to know that I dread this ordeal. I do not fear any man. I only abhor this so-called tradition of gentlemen."

The challenge came as no surprise. Andrew Jackson had warned him to practice his marksmanship at every opportunity. A gentleman in public affairs must stand ready to defend himself in "affairs of honor."

Such things took on ridiculous patterns. The political foe who issued the challenge ducked out of the duel. His second, General William A. White, felt committed to step in. There was no ill feeling between General White and Sam Houston when they faced each other on an early September morning.

"Gentlemen, are you ready?" asked the referee.

Both principals nodded. White's shot went wide. Sam's bullet thudded into the general's groin and the wounded man sank to the ground. "You have severely wounded me," he said weakly as Sam bent over him.

"I am very sorry," Sam said slowly. "But you know it was forced on me."

"I know it and I forgive you."

Sam poured out his grief in a letter to Eliza Allen. To whom else could he reveal his inner feelings? He was disgusted—more so as people applauded his heroism. He voiced his reaction to that from a Nashville rostrum.

"I grieve for General White," he told his listeners. "I pray for his full recovery. And I entreat Almighty God to give me the courage to decline all such challenges in the future."

Some of his closest supporters begged him not to voice such sentiments. The code of gentlemen called for duels. Couldn't Houston quietly accept plaudits for his victory? Andrew Jackson was among those concerned, but Sam was unmoved. General White recovered; his late adversary hailed that as a blessing.

"I could not do anything else," Sam explained to Eliza. "If that makes me a coward, then let my enemies add that to their other trumped-up charges."

Eliza smiled tenderly. She detested duels; all women

did. And this unexpected side of Sam Houston's character thrilled her more than she liked to admit. Perhaps she had been mistaken in her first impression of this huge, tempestuous man who wanted to marry her. Many of his traits would disturb any girl of her background and upbringing. Certainly he would make a possessive, domineering husband. Tennessee had never seen another like him.

The Whig candidate, Newton Cannon, boasted that he would carry East Tennessee. The mountain people, he claimed, opposed the "Jackson crowd" because it was through their influence that the state capital had been moved from Knoxville to Nashville. They would not back Billy Carroll's "errand boy."

Sam answered that taunt with the strong statement that he was no man's proxy. He sought the governorship on his own merits. He traveled through East Tennessee on a dapple-gray stallion, stopping to speak from courthouse steps. He reminded listeners that he had spent his boyhood in these mountains. He had spared these settlements a "bath of blood" by persuading the Cherokees to cede their long-time homelands to the white man.

Back to Nashville rode the tired campaigner. "I have done all I can," he wrote to Eliza Allen. "It is in the laps of the gods."

Returns came in slowly. The first reports caused a demonstration in Cannon's headquarters. The Billy Carroll machine was supposed to control counties in middle Tennessee. It didn't. Cannon took an early lead. As returns came in from the western settlements Sam Houston forged ahead, but it was a narrow margin. If East Tennessee swung into the Whig camp as so many expected . . .

The votes crept in from the hill-country boxes. The

Smoky Mountain folk were going strong for their native son, the younger brother of John and James Houston; the onetime schoolmaster of Maryville!

Houston's margin was 44,426 to 33,410.

He moved his belongings from the Nashville Inn into the governor's mansion.

"It is a lonely place," he wrote Eliza. "It cries out for the soft and refining touch of a lady's hand."

The fruits of victory were sweet indeed, especially since he could believe it a personal victory.

Billy Carroll had been at first amused and then disturbed during the campaign by Houston's claim that he was no man's errand boy. He watched the young governor's progress in office with growing resentment. What if the young whippersnapper refused to return to Congress two years hence, as they had planned! Would he have to challenge the political power of his own protégé? And, just as disturbing, James K. Polk, the congressman selected to serve in Sam's stead for two years, looked like a political comer himself! Carroll appealed to President Jackson for help. None came. Old Hickory refused to take sides in any "family squabble."

Finally Carroll asked Pryor Lea to find out Sam's intentions.

"We have been friends," the former governor said grimly. "But if he fancies himself as his own man—" Carroll left his threat unfinished. But there was no doubt of his intentions.

Lea was not happy with his role as "middleman."

"I am your friend," he told Sam. "If you mean to challenge Carroll, I will be on your side. But I wish there were another solution."

"There isn't," Sam said gravely. "Mr. Carroll may have

made an honest error. He may have thought I would take orders from him. I never have. I have appreciated his backing during these years, but the Democratic party in Tennessee is not his personal property. If he must regard my ambitions as a personal affront, then let him."

"I take it," Lea said slowly, "that you will seek reelection?"

"I certainly shall," Sam said firmly.

Lea sighed. "You could have withheld that declaration. You know that Carroll will start organizing immediately."

"Yes," agreed Sam. "But I would not have it otherwise. Give Mr. Carroll my personal regards."

Carroll calmly accepted the gantlet. "Houston is a strong candidate," he admitted. "He might win, if he doesn't make some grave mistake."

Billy Carroll started his own campaign then and there. But Sam Houston had another campaign to wage before he could turn his mind toward the next election. He still had not won Eliza's consent to be his wife.

And it was January 22, 1829, before she came downstairs on her father's arm and accepted Sam Houston as her husband. The wedding was a rather quiet affair. Only a few guests were invited to the Allen mansion. A Presbyterian minister read the rituals.

The honeymoon was brief, too. Immediately after their turn to the capital, Sam's formal announcement for reelection threw Tennessee into political turmoil. Carroll was already campaigning hard. Could the pupil beat out his master?

Three short weeks later an alarming report reached Colonel Willoughby Williams, the sheriff of Nashville County. He was self-appointed chairman of Governor Houston's campaign for reelection, and he had gotten off to a great beginning. The public showed thrilling response for the young rebel, and waning support for Billy Carroll.

The distressed colonel found Sam alone with Dr. John Shelby, who had known Eliza since infancy. One look at Sam convinced Williams that something momentous had occurred. The young governor was very tired and very troubled.

"Governor, I've heard that—" He stopped, groping for words.

"It is true, my good friend," Sam said gently. "My wife has returned to her parents. We have separated."

The colonel choked. What would this do to Sam's political future? The people of Tennessee were rallying around him, and partly because the world loves a lover.

"It doesn't matter, Colonel," Sam said tonelessly. "I am withdrawing from the campaign. In fact, I am resigning as governor."

"You mean—"

"I mean it. I am leaving Tennessee. I intend to leave alone and at once."

Sheriff Williams gasped. "But—where, Governor? Not back to Washington?"

"Under no circumstances." Sam heaved a deep sigh. "I go to the western territory of the Cherokees," he said slowly, "to the lands I persuaded John Jolly to accept."

How could he explain his feelings and his intended actions? His own brothers had never understood why he fled to the Cherokee lodges when he was sick and troubled. He could trust a Cherokee promise of affection and loyalty. At the moment nothing else mattered.

"But, Governor, your friends—"

"I know. I am deserting my own cause. It can't be helped. There is nothing else to do."

"Governor, you can't do it! Your whole life—man, you're sure to beat Carroll! And General Jackson is fading fast. We're committed to Martin Van Buren in 'thirty-six, but we want you for president in 'forty."

"I know," Sam said. "But I have decided." He turned to Dr. Shelby. "I charge you with a solemn responsibility, sir. You must inform Eliza's family of my action."

"Not I," refused Dr. Shelby. "Not until you have furnished me with a reason."

"There is none."

"There must be."

"If there is," Sam said, rising slowly, "I will carry it to my grave unspoken."

He turned and strode out of the room. The unhappy doctor turned to the distressed sheriff.

"Is there nothing we can do?"

"I don't know," answered Colonel Williams. "I never encountered anything like this before."

"There will be a scandal if he just walks out."

The sheriff nodded. There would be, indeed. Billy Carroll was a shrewd and ruthless politician. He would seize this chance to ruin the young man who had broken out of the traces.

"There will be a scandal," said Colonel Williams, a choke in his voice. "And Sam Houston is walking straight into oblivion."

"Why?" sighed Dr. Shelby. "In God's name, why!"

The sheriff shrugged his shoulders. "He said he would carry the secret to his grave. And, as far as I know, Sam Houston has kept every promise he has ever made."

Colonel Williams reached for his hat. "I'll trail after him," he decided. "He'll need my help if he tries to slip off unseen. That's about all I can do for him."

"You are his friend, Colonel," murmured Dr. Shelby.

"Aren't you?"

"I don't know," hesitated the physician. "Eliza and her family come first with me. And surely there's a better way of doing this."

"There is," Colonel Williams said gruffly. "But Sam is calling this turn. This is his way of doing it. I reckon it's his right, too—he'll pay the fiddler for this little dance. Lordee, how he'll pay for it!"

The Nashville sheriff followed Sam into the darkness outside. He overtook the governor and offered his help. Sam accepted. Reports were spreading like wildfire, and Colonel Williams thought it best that they move quietly along Nashville streets. The captain of a river packet, the *Red Rover,* agreed to transport an anonymous passenger to the Ohio River. Sam boarded the vessel alone. The packet had barely left the wharf when an angry group of citizens came in pursuit. The sheriff reasoned with them. Sam Houston was no fugitive from justice. He was fleeing from a personal tragedy, not a crime. But these assurances fell on deaf ears. There was bound to be an ugly side to this story, people argued.

The *Red Rover* moved slowly against the current of the Tennessee River. Two of Eliza's kinsmen galloped ahead and stood waiting when the packet docked at Clarksville to refuel.

Houston came out of his stateroom immediately. He stood unmoved as the two Allens threatened to shoot him down. Both were heavily armed. They demanded to know if there was any truth in reports that Sam had "detected our sister in crime."

Sam stirred. He would answer that question gladly. "Publish in the Nashville newspapers," he said coldly, "that if any wretch dares to utter a word against the purity of Mrs. Houston I will come back and write the libel in his heart's blood."

That satisfied the angry kinsmen, partially at least. They allowed Sam to travel on into self-imposed exile.

He looked after them bitterly. Why had they come? Was this misunderstanding so mysterious? Eliza was a young, impressionable woman, little more than a girl, and she had been overwhelmed by the force of her suitor's personality. Marriages, however, must be based on more solid foundations. Her wounds would heal in his absence, and a girlish mistake need not blight her life. That was her side of the story and she could tell it her own way. He would carry his side to his grave unspoken, as he had told Williams and Shelby.

He paced the small deck of the *Red Rover*. He knew only one place to turn. What would he find in the West? He remembered a bit of Cherokee mythology. The western skies held death for the red man but glorious opportunity for his white brothers.

Another Indian legend gave some comfort to the westward traveler. Man needed the fire, and the raven fetched a burning ember. Co-lon-neh was scorched in the effort. Wasn't he Co-lon-neh, the Raven? He had suffered pain in his efforts to serve mankind.

The way west was long, by a flatboat down the Mississippi to Memphis, by horseback to Fort Smith, along a rough military road to the Indian territory.

Runners sped ahead. Almost half of Oo-loo-te-ka's clan met the prodigal at the trading post of Walter Webber, a half-breed who had been elected an official of the Cherokee nation.

John Jolly would not allow a simple reception.

"My son," he declaimed, "eleven winters have passed

since we met. I have heard you were a great chief among your people . . . I have heard that a dark cloud has fallen on the white path you were walking. I am glad of it . . . it was done by the Great Spirit. We are in trouble and the Great Spirit has sent you to give us counsel. My wigwam is yours . . . my home is yours . . . my people are yours. Rest with us."

★ 6

A Cherokee Defends His Honor

THE CHEROKEE THERAPY SUCCEEDED AGAIN. LONG AGO the Indians had persuaded a moody, unhappy youth to help them win a ball game. Now John Jolly's people convinced a disillusioned man that the Cherokee Nation needed his strong voice.

Oo-loo-te-ka's people were in trouble. He was principal chief of the Cherokees now, groping with the worries of all western clans. White settlers were invading their domain. The savage Pawnees and Comanches disputed possession of the hunting grounds. The Osages made war on another front. And scheming, unscrupulous agents defrauded the Cherokees at every turn.

The annual indemnity owed by the United States was supposed to be paid in gold. It wasn't. Major E. W. Duval handed out certificates of payment—scraps of paper which could be redeemed. The average Cherokee attached little value to pieces of paper. Indians quickly exchanged certificates for trade goods, never understanding that white traders were allowing them much less than face value.

The Cherokees needed Sam Houston. Oo-loo-te-ka

was convinced the Great White Father knew nothing about the misdeeds and inefficiencies of his agents. Co-lon-neh could plead the Cherokee cause eloquently and with dignity. They must nurse the wounded warrior back to health and send him back to battle. Indians knew patience. They knew the spirit healed even more slowly than flesh.

Sam agreed to serve. "I am no longer a white man in anything but color," he told John Jolly. "I shall no longer think as a white man. I have left those who were my people and joined those who are."

Nothing could gratify Oo-loo-te-ka more. Indian agents were not so pleased. There were laws regulating a United States citizen's activities with Indian tribes which were government wards. Major Duval considered Sam's arrest.

The Cherokee nation forestalled him. On October 21, 1839, Sam was granted formal Cherokee citizenship. John Jolly struggled with a letter to President Andrew Jackson:

> GREAT FATHER!
>
> My son the Raven came to me last spring. . . . He has walked straight. . . . His path is not crooked. . . . He is now leaving me to meet his *White* Father, Gen. Jackson, and look upon him and I hope he will take him by the hand and keep him as near to his heart as I have done. He is beloved by all my people. . . .

Did any ambassador ever approach Washington with a more eloquent letter of introduction?

Two warriors accompanied the emissary eastward. Major Duval intercepted the party.

"Is it true you are going to Washington to make charges against me as an agent?"

"It is true," Sam said.

Duval turned livid. "What charges do you intend to make? What proof do you have?"

"Have you pen and paper?"

The agent provided both. Sam quickly listed the complaints he meant to voice in the capital. Profiteering, cheating, breaking faith— Sam spared no words.

"Now, sir," Sam coldly said, "please put your initial to this text. I want officials in Washington to know you are informed of the charges."

"Do you think President Jackson will hear you?" Duval's voice held scorn, but he was worried. "You have lost any influence in Washington. You have given up your American citizenship. You claim to be an Indian, sir —a Cherokee. Well, see that you go to Washington as an Indian. Don't try to parade yourself as any paragon of virtues."

"That I won't, sir," Sam shot back. "I have never denied my failings. But I have always spoken the truth. Not even my enemies have denied my honor."

He turned on his heel and strode away. His Cherokee escort turned back at the limits of Indian territory. Sam traveled on alone, brooding over Duval's scornful words. Would President Jackson refuse to see him? Would he meet derision everywhere he turned? Whispers would fly ahead of him; he could be sure of that. The gossip would be uglier than the truth, too. The easier course, he mused, was to turn back. But he gave that scant consideration. The Cherokees trusted him. He had their confidence and their prayers. He recalled John Jolly's message to the President. "My son the Raven . . . has walked straight. His path is not crooked."

But he decided against announcing himself to anyone in Tennessee. No one recognized the lone horseman plodding eastward. Sam even managed to visit President

Jackson's plantation without being recognized. He cut a walking cane from a hickory sapling there. No tree in the Indian territory matched Tennessee hickory.

Then he rode on.

Washington presented a dreary appearance that January. Its streets were nearly deserted, which pleased Sam. His arrival would create enough attention; let it start slowly. He dismounted before Brown's Tavern. Ignoring curious stares, he strode directly to the registration desk.

"Lodging, please," he told the startled manager. "I will be here an indefinite time."

The proprietor hesitated. Sam stood tall and menacing in his Cherokee attire—yellow leggings, breechclout, hunting coat and bright blanket. The manager's first impulse was to deny accommodations. His hotel didn't accept all guests. Then he relented. His visitor had once been Andrew Jackson's favorite lieutenant. Who could be sure how Sam Houston stood with the President? Even Sam himself wondered. Would President Jackson receive his former protégé?

All of Washington wondered and waited. The tense gossips knew when Sam formally requested an appointment. Many stories about Sam had reached the President, few of them complimentary. Surely the Chief Executive wouldn't open his door to a man who had renounced his United States citizenship!

But President Jackson did just that. He greeted Sam warmly and listened closely to Sam's words.

"I shall look into it," he promised. "You will hear from me."

What had the exiled man proposed to the President? It was soon common knowledge. Jackson summoned several government officials immediately, including the Secretary of War. Major John Eaton's lips tightened as the Chief Executive explained that he had just conferred with Sam Houston.

"He came to ask about our contract for supplying the Cherokees. What are we doing for those people now, Major?"

The Secretary had his figures ready. "We are negotiating a new contract for supplying rations to the Cherokee Nation," he said. "The present cost is twenty-five cents a day. But the Indians aren't satisfied. We are calling for new bids, and setting forth new requirements." A smile touched Major Eaton's face. He respected Sam Houston, too. "I'm sure that the new contracts will satisfy Mr. Houston."

The President nodded. "They must." Jackson had not forgotten who had persuaded the Indians to move west. "General Houston wishes to contract for their subsistence himself. He has accumulated quite a bit of information concerning costs, methods of distribution, and so on. He offers to provide a superior ration for eighteen cents a day. That would save our government some twelve thousand dollars a year."

So it would—a saving of seven cents daily for each Indian moved west of the Mississippi. All the government officials present exchanged surprised looks. So this was why Sam Houston had returned to Washington. He meant to wangle a contract through the President!

Well, Sam Houston wouldn't get it. Duff Green decided that immediately. He was proprietor of the *United States Telegraph* and charter member of Andrew Jackson's "kitchen cabinet," that unofficial group of friends and advisers who helped the President make administrative decisions.

Eighteen cents was no bargain, said Green. Beef bought on the hoof in Illinois and Missouri could be distributed for much less. General Green guessed six cents to be a fair price.

President Jackson hid his reaction. This bore out what Sam Houston had said. The United States government was paying too much for too little. The Chief Executive pretended to show no further interest in negotiations for a new contract. The low bidder proved to be John Shackleford of St. Louis, at eight cents. The business took several days.

Sam appeared dejected when informed that he had lost out in the bidding, but he was neither disappointed nor surprised. He hadn't wanted any such contract in the first place. He was no tradesman. Hadn't he fled from a store to the Cherokee Nation? His play for a contract was only a gesture to convince the President that government funds were being wasted in the Indian territory.

He told Jackson so. The President's eyes twinkled. He had guessed as much. Sam had lost none of his political shrewdness.

"Now," Sam proposed, "let us take up the matter of corrupt Indian agents." He produced the list of charges against Duval and four other Indian agents.

Duff Green was the self-appointed spokesman of the faction opposing Sam. These men had their own plans for Andrew Jackson's successor as leader of the Democratic party. They didn't want Sam Houston back in the picture. Get him out of Washington quickly—send him back to his adopted Indians!

Sam's eyes gleamed as he bargained with Green and Eaton. Oo-loo-te-ka would never understand how these concessions came about, and Sam wouldn't bother to explain. The Cherokees would never understand the white man's politics, but their emissary did and he pressed his advantage. Five Indian agents were dismissed. Henceforth the Cherokees would be paid their annuity in solid money, not certificates.

Sam mounted his horse and rode away. He had made new political enemies, he mused. He had rekindled old jealous fires. He couldn't help smiling as his pony jogged along the western turnpike. More important, perhaps, was what he had accomplished for himself. He was finished as a political leader only if he chose to be. He relaxed in the saddle and allowed daydreams to form. Was it too late to dream of the presidency? He heaved a deep sigh. Of course it was. He mustn't turn giddy over this small triumph. He had done only a small thing in the eyes of Washington; even less, perhaps, as Tennessee estimated political victories. He had won out because of his nuisance value. It did not suit Andrew Jackson's other lieutenants to have a Cherokee interloper so welcome in the White House. They had conceded this much to be rid of him.

There was little change in his personal situation. He was a hero only to the few hundred survivors of a fading Indian nation. He decided to buy land and set up permanent residence with the Cherokees. He must do something to combat the loneliness that seemed inevitable.

The new Indian agents proved no better. The new contractors were as eager for profits as the old ones. A Cherokee delegation returned to Washington the next year. Sam authored their petition and sat between Black Coat and Opoth-ley-ahola, venerable leader of the Creeks. He meant to advise his Indians brothers but to avoid being the central figure. There was no need for Duff Green, Martin Van Buren and other ambitious

Democrats to fear him. His mother lay buried in the Tennessee hills. His last tie was broken with his native country.

The grievances were the same, but events took on a different pattern. This time Congress was in session. Discussions were not limited to private conferences in the White House. Whig orators saw an opportunity to make political capital out of Sam's second appearance as a Cherokee emissary.

This time—to avoid attention—he had put aside Indian regalia. He had borrowed funds from a friendly Tennesseean, James K. Polk, and outfitted himself with cutaway coat, waistcoat, tight trousers and brown beaver hat. He assured all who wondered that he was there only as an adviser.

But he heard reports of the Whig political strategy immediately. He couldn't believe it. Why, such talk linked him with Green and John C. Calhoun of South Carolina, Democrats who had always been his personal enemies. Sam took a seat in the gallery on March 31, 1832, and shortly heard his name spoken by William Stanbury, a representative from Ohio. Sam had never met him, but this congressman, speaking on personal privilege, insinuated that Sam and the "Secretary of War had conspired to gain a fraudulent contract for Indian rations!"

Fraud! Dishonesty! Conspiracy with former Secretary John Eaton! Nothing was further from the truth. Sam listened a few minutes, then posted himself in the corridor outside the House chamber. He would deal personally with this Stanbury!

James Polk saw Sam pacing the floor and guessed his intentions.

"No, Sam," begged Polk. "You can't start a ruckus here. Think of the scandal. Come with me."

Sam shook his head. What did he care about scandal? Hadn't he lived with it for four years?

"But you'll hurt the President," argued the desperate Polk. "You can't do that. Andrew Jackson has meant too much to you."

Sam's jaw clinched. That was true. Congressman Polk had used the only argument which could have moved him. He allowed himself to be led away, but he had no intention of letting Stanbury's charges stand.

"I have been called many things," he told Polk, "but never dishonest. No other man has charged that I have stolen or lied. Mr. Stanbury is not through with me."

Friends warned the Ohio congressman, who pretended to make light of the situation. Surely a man who had served as governor of Tennessee wouldn't attack him on the street! But William Stanbury made sure he carried a pistol at all times. Why try to apply the usual standards of human conduct to Sam Houston! And the Ohioan carefully avoided places where he was apt to meet Sam Houston.

It was thirteen days before their paths crossed. Sam was walking back to Brown's Tavern after a visit with Senator Grundy. He recognized the man crossing Pennsylvania Avenue.

"Are you Mr. Stanbury?" he asked politely.

"Yes, sir."

"Then you are a damned rascal," snapped Sam. He was carrying the hickory cane cut from a Tennessee sapling and crashed it against the congressman's head. Stanbury threw up one arm to ward off the blows, at the same time turning his back to his assailant while fumbling for his pistol. Sam bore his adversary backward, pummeling him with all his might. When Stanbury finally managed to extract his pistol, he pressed it against Sam's chest and squeezed the trigger. The gun-lock snapped but the charge didn't explode. Sam knocked the gun from Stanbury's hand, dealt out more blows with the hickory cudgel and stalked away.

Repercussions came immediately. Editor Green gave the beating feature play in his *United States Telegraph*. He and Calhoun were finally and officially "out" with President Jackson. The smoldering resentment against Tennessee domination flamed into open revolt. The House of Representatives moved to arrest and try Sam Houston for "murderous assault" on one of its members.

By what right did they arrest a Cherokee citizen? James K. Polk thundered out the question. He was Andrew Jackson's spokesman in the House now. He had stepped into Sam's shoes when the young congressman had conceded his chances of following Old Hickory into the White House. Polk was indignant at the way Sam was being humiliated. He persuaded Francis Scott Key, the famous author of "The Star Spangled Banner," to represent the defendant. But Sam was not willing to let another man speak for him. He cross-examined Stanbury himself.

"You charged me with fraud," Sam thundered. "Did you have any proof when you uttered that statement? Do you have any proof now?"

Stanbury was reluctant to answer. The House of Representatives voted that he must.

"It was no part of my intention," he said lamely, "to impute fraud to General Houston."

Eager spectators packed the galleries, listening spell-bound to Sam's ringing statement of his innocence.

"Mr. Speaker," he said slowly, "I stand arraigned for the first time on charges of violating my country's laws.

I disclaim utterly any motive unworthy of an honorable man."

He faced the galleries. "I can never forget," he said, "that reputation, however limited, is the high boon of heaven. . . . Though the plowshare of ruin has been driven over me and laid waste to my brightest hopes . . . I have only to say

> 'I seek no sympathies, nor need;
> The thorns which I have reaped are of the tree
> I planted; they have torn me and I bleed.' "

The long trial dragged to a close. Sam rose again in his own defense. He pointed dramatically to the flag draping the portrait of the Marquis de Lafayette, the beloved French volunteer in the American Revolution.

"Sir, so long as that flag shall bear aloft its glittering stars . . . so long, I trust, shall the rights of American citizens be preserved safe and unimpaired—'til discord shall wreck the spheres—the grand march of time shall cease—and not one fragment of all creation be left to chafe the bosom of eternity's waves."

That concluded his defense. The House of Representatives acted quickly. All it could do was censure Sam for using physical violence on one of its members. It did that, and the Speaker voiced mild reprimand. But he spoke empty words. The nation's press resounded with praise of Sam's honorable stand.

An old friend, the actor Junius Booth, came forward to embrace him. "Houston," he said shakily, "take my laurels."

The acclaim left Sam a little dizzy. Could he believe these demonstrations? Had he regained in these hectic days all he had lost? Did he dare revive old dreams and plunge along the same path he had abandoned?

An older, wiser man said no. President Jackson admitted his delight, but he added tersely, "You invoked the blessing of a flag, Sam. You wrapped yourself in its hallowed folds. Was that the thing to do? Is it *your* flag?"

Sam's eyes dropped. He couldn't answer this with any blazing oratory. Here was an accusation he could not deny.

"It is *my* flag," he said humbly.

"Then renew your service to it," snapped Jackson. "There is much to be done in the West—for America, not the Cherokees alone. The West is an endless empire which we have yet to win."

Sam took a deep breath. "I am at your service, Mr. President," he said softly—and gratefully, *very* gratefully.

★ 7

The Challenge of Texas

REMEMBERING HIS LATIN, SAM COMPARED THE RED RIVER to the Rubicon. But his circumstances differed greatly from Julius Caesar's. Caesar had plunged into the Rubicon at the head of a triumphant army; Sam breasted the Red's tide alone. Nevertheless he believed the comparison appropriate. Caesar had crossed the Rubicon to gain new laurels. Sam was convinced the same fate awaited him in the Mexican province of Texas.

The date was December 1, 1832. Sam meant never to forget it. He intended to remember, too, his first impression of Texas. It was a vacant plain spotted with patches of jack-oak and dirty red grass. It was lonely country, quite unimpressive. Yet restless or ambitious Americans had schemed for its conquest for a full generation.

Even longer, for Aaron Burr had meant to envelop this western country in his grandiose schemes. I have a personal interest in this land, reflected Sam. His father had invested precious dollars in Burr's undertaking. Two other Americans had marched into Texas at the head of land-grabbing expeditions. Sam knew the results of both. The Magee-Gutierrez venture had collapsed at Bexar. Dr. James Long had died in a Spanish prison after proclaiming the organization of a republic of Texas.

Andrew Jackson had shown interest in Texas for a decade. First he had claimed that the territory between the Rio Grande and the Red River was acquired in the Louisiana Purchase. Then he had tried to purchase Texas from the Republic of Mexico.

Now Texas, in population, was more American than Mexican. Mexico had removed its bans against foreign immigration in 1825. Several Americans had contracted to bring in settlers. These were called *empresarios*. They received land concessions from the government and would be entitled to bounty lands when they had met their contracts. Sam had studied the *empresario* contract issued to Sterling J. Robertson of Tennessee and intended to inform himself about the others. He must learn all details if he were to satisfy Andrew Jackson's curiosity.

Texas—the word did have a magic ring! Sam could close his eyes and put new belief in the old Cherokee legend. The West was a happy land for the white man, and the time had come for him to grapple with his own destiny.

He followed a rough road southward—little more than a winding trail. The distance ahead seemed incredible. Nacogdoches was a hundred and eighty miles away. It was considered the gateway to Texas, the easternmost outpost of Mexico's authority. All that Texas was, or might be, sprawled farther on. President Jackson desired a full, firsthand account of conditions within the whole province. Sam must ride a thousand lonely miles to form such personal impressions.

At last he reached Nacogdoches, a sprawling little settlement already steeped in history. Its stone fort was over a century old. French soldiers had occupied it for a time; so had Sam's countrymen. Two "republics" had been proclaimed by adventurous Americans—the first by James Long; the second by Haden Edwards, formerly of Kentucky. But Sam was concerned, at the moment, with the problem of lodging. He was dead weary. He breathed a prayer of gratitude for the rough inn known as "Brown's Tavern." It was a far cry from Brown's Tavern in Washington but the best available. He found the only other tavern crowded with Mexican soldiers and a fat woman who smoked a cigar as she strummed a guitar.

He gave his name and spread his blankets on the floor—Texas taverns offered a roof but no bed. He slept solidly for nine hours, then ate, shaved and donned fresh linen. He knew one Nacogdoches resident to contact—merchant Adolphus Sterne.

Sterne proved to be a pleasant, well-educated German. Sam was not surprised to learn that he was *alcalde* of Nacogdoches—its mayor.

"And what brings you to Texas, General Houston?"

"To consider the possibilities," Sam said casually. He was a homeless man at present, he added. "I am looking for a place to settle. What are the prospects for another lawyer?"

"Well," said Sterne with a smile, "we have them. You will meet some interesting gentlemen at Velasco, if you travel so far."

"I will," Houston said with a nod.

He learned a great deal from Sterne. Nacogdoches was one of two Spanish settlements in the area. Bexar, the other, was populated almost entirely by Mexicans. The settlements between those two were American. Immigrants had established the ports of Anahuac and Velasco. Mexican authorities were attempting to enforce customs regulations.

"That always creates dissension," mused Sterne. Sam

nodded, remembering the beginnings of the American Revolution.

"How many immigrants from the United States are settled in Texas?"

Sterne shook his head. The exact number was uncertain. Some American-born settlers dated their residence in Texas back to the 1820's. "Those who slipped into the country and have lived quietly—Mexico has allowed them to stay; has even approved their occupation of lands. And not all immigrants since 1825 have registered with Mexican authorities as the law requires. A group from your native state, General, circled around Nacogdoches. Their route through the lower Sabine River country is known as the Tennessee Trail."

Sam nodded. He knew a smattering of such things already. An estimated eight thousand United States-born immigrants were supposedly living along the Brazos and Colorado rivers. How long would such men accept Mexican authority?

Sam rode on to San Felipe de Austin. The road was called a *camino real,* a king's highway. Spanish *conquistadores* had blazed the route a century before, but it was still a trail, winding, deep-rutted. Timber grew thick—oak, sweetgum, sycamore, loblolly pine. Sam studied a map by firelight that night. The main rivers of Texas flowed eastward into the Gulf of Mexico. Their basins reminded him of Tennessee. Black bottom country, good for cotton and early corn. The climate was milder than along the Cumberland or the Hatchie.

San Felipe was a bustling little village on the Brazos. The settlement, the capital of Stephen F. Austin's concession or colony, was seven years old. Sam had heard of Austin's colonizing venture. A dozen other men had wangled similar *empresario* contracts, but Austin was the most successful. His pamphlets were circulated in almost every state of the Union. Most of his settlers came from the South, but New England and Pennsylvania had also sent emigrants to the Brazos. A New York company was quite interested in a Texas land promotion. Sam meant to contact them if and when he located his law office.

Stephen Austin wasn't in San Felipe. He had traveled to Mexico City to convince Mexican authorities that not all newcomers were troublemakers. Sam tensed. He must learn the details of all demonstrations against Mexican rule. Andrew Jackson expected a revolt.

Tennessee had supplied many of the late immigrants. "And you know our people," Jackson had said wryly. "They are quick to resent strong authority. The government which tries to curb their individuality won't stay in power long."

Sam thought of that as he met San Felipe's leading citizens—Samuel Williams, the Kuykendall brothers, the Jacks, Jared Groce. There were emigrants from Tennessee and other southern states. They differed in personalities and ambitions, but Sam detected the same restlessness in each. They wanted local governments. They wanted a state organization. They resented being remote from provincial politics. They were Americans, mused Sam. They hadn't changed by crossing a river. Why should they? How many rivers had these rugged families crossed in fifty years? The Tennessee first; then the Cumberland, and the Mississippi. After all, the Red was just another river to swim.

James Bowie confirmed that impression. Sam traveled another two hundred miles to meet Bowie, a Louisianan who had learned more about Texas than any other American—unless it was Peter Bean of Nacogdoches, whom Sam distrusted. Bowie had married the daughter of a Mexican vice-governor. He had acquired huge tracts of land and had learned about a secret gold deposit sacred to the Lipan Apaches.

A gentleman in appearance and manner, Bowie was also one of the deadliest duelists anywhere and had popularized the bowie knife as a fighting weapon. He spoke Spanish fluently and was trusted by both Mexicans and Americans. It was difficult to believe in Bowie until a man met him; from then on, there was no doubting him. He was an engaging, straightforward adventurer.

"There could be peaceful organization of Texas under Mexican authorities," Bowie said thoughtfully. "But it won't happen. The two races of people are too different. The Spanish believe in absolute authority. It's their heritage. The proprietor is master of his domain. He acknowledges only the national authorities. He will obey a viceroy but not an *alcalde*. He does not know much about town governments, and less about county and state authorities." The handsome blond man sighed. "I would say, General, that separation is inevitable. You have come to the right place at the right time."

"I am here as a private citizen," disclaimed Sam. "If I am impressed with Texas, I shall settle here. I am a lawyer by profession."

"Yes, you are," agreed Bowie with a faint smile. He looked around. "Time is opportunity here for any sort of man. Already all sorts have come west." His voice tightened. "But don't sell the Mexicans too short, General. This is 1832. Aaron Burr plotted to take over Texas more than a generation ago. He sent Philip Nolan across the Sabine, and Nolan lost his head. Next came Augustus Magee. He helped raise the green flag over this very town of Bexar. Magee died rather mysteriously. Some of his associates didn't. Their heads were lopped off and displayed on Spanish pikes. James Long died in a Mexican prison. The Mexicans are gentle, sleepy people, but they can be aroused. And theirs can be a savage cruelty."

"I shall remember that, Friend Bowie," promised Sam. "But I am no land grabber. I would not accept any authority which was not voted me by a free people."

Bexar received Sam hospitably. Don Juan Veramendi, vice-governor and Bowie's father-in-law, was especially courteous. Sam drank in the sights of the gleaming stone and adobe town, founded a century before by emigrants from the Canary Islands. He gave brief attention to the idle mission of San Antonio de Valero. It seemed unimportant at the time that previous revolutions had centered around this mission. Some Bexar people called it the "Alamo," Spanish for cottonwood, because of the cottonwood grove nearby.

The social life intrigued him. He appreciated Spanish arias played on guitars, señoritas in flashy dress and with swirling, provocative fans. It had been a long time since Sam Houston had enjoyed mixed company. He hadn't realized until now how lonely these years had been. Riding back to Nacogdoches, he resolved against any more self-exile. He craved the companionship of his own kind. He was in Texas, where few questions were asked about a newcomer's past. All sorts of men had come to Texas. Some had fled debts, and some were fugitives from justice. Others had left nothing worse than personal disappointment behind. Sam could become one of those. He had come to Texas an unhappy man but with his personal honor unsullied. Let Congressman Stanbury examine his own scars if he doubted it.

Sam returned to Nacogdoches on February 12, 1833.

He leased a vacant cabin and spread his blankets on the floor. He borrowed quill and paper from Adolphus Sterne and wrote a long letter to Andrew Jackson.

History has recorded his exact words:

General Jackson:
Dear Sir—

Having been so far as Bexar, in the province of Texas . . . I am in possession of some information that . . . may be calculated to forward your views, if you should entertain any, touching the acquisition by the United States.

That such a measure is desired by nineteen-twentieths of the population, I cannot doubt. . . . Mexico is involved in Civil War . . . the people of Texas are determined to form a State government, and to separate from Coahuila, and unless Mexico is soon returned to order . . . Texas will remain separate from the Confederacy of Mexico.

She has already beaten and repelled all the troops of Mexico from her soil. . . . She can defend herself against the whole power of Mexico, for really Mexico is powerless and penniless. . . . Her want of money, taken in connection with the course which Texas *must and will* adopt, will render a transfer of Texas to some power inevitable. . . .

Now is a very important crisis for Texas—England is pressing her suit—for its citizens will resist if any transfer should be made of them to any power but the United States. . . . My opinion is that Texas, by her members in the Convention, will by 1st of April declare all that country (north of the Rio Grande) as Texas proper, and form a State Constitution. I expect to be present at that Convention and will apprise you of the course adopted. . . . I may make Texas my abiding place . . . but I *will never forget* the country of my birth. I will notify from this point the Commissioners of the Indians at Fort Gibson of my success, which will reach you through the War Department. . . .

Your friend and obedient servant,
SAM HOUSTON

Time has confirmed the general accuracy of that report. Texas was moving into a crisis indeed. History was in the making. Sam knew it and resolved to be a leader in it.

But he minimized one important condition. Apparently Jim Bowie's warnings hadn't made much of an impression. For all their complacency, their poverty, their disorganized internal affairs, the Mexicans were formidable. They had fought for Texas before, and would again.

★ 8

Revolution Is Born

SAM FOUND NACOGDOCHES BUZZING WITH EXCITEMENT. A revolution in Mexico had swept new leaders into power. General López de Santa Anna was the new president of Mexico. He was a military hero of so-called "liberal" leanings. Now was the time for Texas to sue for separation from Coahuila and for redress of all grievances. Texans had taken little part in Mexican politics, but those who were active had supported Santa Anna.

"Can we consider you a Texas citizen?" Sterne asked the question point-blank.

"Why?" countered Sam.

"If you are," said the merchant, "we want you as our delegate to the convention."

Sam knew that the settlement would send delegates to a meeting at San Felipe on April 1. He meant to attend. But as an official delegate—why not some other Nacogdoches man, one who had lived here a time? Why not Sterne himself?

"I am a merchant," shrugged the German. "Politics is not for me. As for the others here . . ." he smiled. "You must remember, General, that every conspiracy against Spain and Mexico began here." He pointed to the old stone fort. "Four times men have barricaded that place against government troops. A man from Nacogdoches isn't trusted. He is expected to be either a traitor or a horse thief. You are neither."

Sam's eyes twinkled. Such charges had never been voiced to his knowledge.

"If you are financially pressed," Sterne said awkwardly, "I can advance you funds."

Sam nodded. His funds were quite low. He needed a new wardrobe, another horse, a saddle. And he must find a more suitable shelter, one with at least two rooms. One could serve as an office. And, he mused, his lack of a library forestalled professional success. No texts on Mexican laws were available.

He rode south again, this time on a spirited chestnut, his saddlebags bulging with spare linen and other personal accessories. The road was rough and poorly marked, but not as lonely as the *camino real* from San Felipe to Bexar. Sam circled around more than one creaking wagon and some small caravans. The tide of immigration, he mused, was just forming. Let one family move west and a dozen followed. Most left hurriedly without the careful preparations his mother and brothers had made. He smiled as he recalled the gleaming Conestoga. He had left Virginia without any qualms, eager for the new challenges of the Tennessee backwoods. He had wanted to see the rugged hills which had given birth to the Free State of Franklin. Now his curiosity led him along a rougher trail, fifteen hundred miles farther west. Would Texas be another "free state"?

San Felipe was wholly different from Bexar. The houses in the American settlement were log structures carefully smoothed and joined. Each boasted a stone fireplace with an open section or "dog run." He observed tidiness and industry everywhere. The women did it, he mused—women such as his mother had been. He recalled his uncle's complaint. "When a woman wants order, she doesn't give a hoot who won the war or who is king."

But men did. Some had already reached San Felipe. There would be fifty-five delegates in all, including representatives from Bexar. Sam quickly appreciated the significance of that delegation. Mexican-born citizens of Texas also wanted separation from Coahuila, but not annexation to the United States—he must watch his words.

He took his choice of two inns and ate roasted venison and biscuits. The traveler found familiar foodstuffs along the Brazos. Steamers from New Orleans put in at the port of Velasco regularly. Had there been any more protests against Mexican customs officials? Had the new administration appointed new customs men? Sam learned that it had. Apparently that ruckus was settled for the time being.

"General Houston?"

"Yes, sir."

"Do you remember me, sir?"

Houston hesitated. The stocky, black-haired man looked familiar, but Sam wasn't sure.

"William Wharton, sir. I met you in Nashville several times."

"Of course," Sam said quickly. Wharton had been a planter and a strong supporter of both Jackson and himself.

"I had hoped to find you alone," explained Wharton. "I was happy to learn that you are an official delegate from Nacogdoches. What do you know of our situation?"

"Very little." Sam felt that was not quite true, but he was eager to learn more. And the way to learn was to let the other man talk.

"There are fifty-five delegates," Wharton said. "The

majority are comparative newcomers to Texas. They don't hold with Stephen F. Austin—that we should sue humbly for better treatment. They are ready to *demand* rights and liberties. And if they don't get them—if Santa Anna isn't receptive to our petitions—"

Sam nodded. The new Mexican administration faced a positive choice. Either grant separate statehood to the Texas settlers or prepare for revolution.

"I believe the time has come to take a strong stand," said Sam.

"Then, sir," cried Wharton, "you are our choice for chairman of the convention. It is high time we showed Mr. Austin that we do not like his methods. He isn't our sort of leader. He is overcautious, even hesitant. A fine man, surely; these settlements stand as a monument to his vision and industry. But the time has come—"

Sam raised his hand. The time was here, he declared, but he wasn't the proper leader. Consider the effect in the United States, he argued—in England and France. Sam Houston was known as Andrew Jackson's protégé. Mexico could say that the United States President had sent Sam to Texas to form a rebellion. England and France would believe it. Both nations might lend Mexico money to suppress insurrection on the Brazos.

"I am not your man," repeated Sam. "I am with you, but I am too new on the scene. I suggest, sir, that you offer yourself as presiding officer."

"I will do so reluctantly," said Wharton. "Politics is out of my field." He frowned in sudden thought. "We had counted on you to draft a proposed state constitution. Would that embarrass you?"

"I think not," Sam decided. "I shall have a draft ready by noon, sir."

He wrote diligently until past midnight. The idea did

not strike him as absurd. He had been in Texas less than six months, but he felt competent to outline the framework of a state government. And why not? Who among these immigrants had studied a state constitution so closely?

He met Stephen F. Austin the next day. Sam's first impression was unfavorable—Austin did not appear to have a strong personality. He was a slight man, cautious of manner and speech, even a little retiring. Yet there was no denying the greatness of his work. Austin had brought a thousand American families to his colonies on the Brazos and the Colorado and had organized local governments, gradually yielding the absolute authority tendered him by Mexico. His voice was heard often in the opening minutes of the convention. He believed an understanding could be reached with Mexico and discouraged any action which would cause Mexico to doubt the loyalty of the new citizens.

Houston listened intently to every word. Fully a dozen of these fifty-five delegates were from Tennessee. The majority had come to Texas since 1830. They weren't accustomed to Austin's direction. To use a homespun phrase, they were ready to kick out of the traces.

And there was no doubt they needed a leader. Sam's eyes gleamed. He must be patient and allow himself to be pushed forward. Sighing gently, he sank lower on his cane-bottomed chair. Hadn't he learned patience in these thirty-nine years—each and every lesson a painful one?

Austin was the first nominee for chairman. A hush fell over the room. Sam tensed. Would there be no opposition? Finally Peter Grayson arose. Houston had known of him for years. He had practiced law in Kentucky before emigrating to Texas.

"At first thought," said Grayson, "Mr. Austin seems the logical choice. He has led us through many trying times. But Mr. Austin is also our inevitable choice as spokesman in Mexico City. He speaks Spanish fluently. He has influence in the capital. The responsibilities of the convention won't end with this session. A chairman must of necessity serve as nominal head of our local councils. His duty will be here. For that reason I nominate William H. Wharton."

Sam nursed his smile. Grayson's words were well put. Wharton was elected and Austin appointed to lay the convention's requests before Santa Anna.

"I accept, of course," said the sincere Austin. "But let me warn you that negotiations with Mexico take time. And let me beg you to practice patience in my absence. Don't throw away, in a rash moment, all we have won. We have our lands . . . our homes . . . our integrity. Our guarantees of personal freedom will come in time."

Sam's proposed constitution was adopted by a unanimous vote. Few knew he was the author. He wanted it so. He musn't appear too eager to become the leader of these frustrated colonists. Many things must be done before Sam was ready for such responsibilities.

The first was to put his own affairs in order. He was indebted for the very clothes he wore. Returning to Nacogdoches, he gratefully accepted Mr. Sterne's offer of hospitality. The other choice was Brown's Tavern, which was not really a choice at all; for the man who had penned a state constitution couldn't pay even reasonable charges.

Conditions had changed by early autumn of 1835. Stephen F. Austin's treatment by Mexico had angered even the most cautious settler. He was held in prison for eighteen months and then was sent back without redress of Texas arguments.

Austin begged for patience, but made little impression. Neither did the leading attorney of Nacogdoches. Sam could claim that distinction now, for he had acquired influential clients, principally the Texas and Galveston Bay Land Company. By July, 1835, he had accumulated four thousand acres of Red River land. His clientele included capitalists in New Orleans and Washington as well as in New York. He had traveled extensively in their interests. No Texas settler had a wider personal acquaintance; none could claim more influence.

But Sam couldn't delay revolution any longer. He tried manfully. New arrivals reached Texas daily. The tide of United States immigration had doubled in two years.

Texas grew stronger all along. Every diplomatic failure helped. President Jackson again tried to purchase Texas for the United States. He was rebuffed coldly. Santa Anna's dictatorial ways embittered sincere and influential Mexican patriots. The most eloquent voice calling for immediate action belonged to Lorenzo de Zavala, who had helped elect Santa Anna president. De Zavala had moved his family to a *rancho* on the San Jacinto River. More Tennesseeans crossed the Red River and looked to Nacogdoches for leadership. Sterling C. Robertson quarreled with Austin over land titles. James Collingsworth proposed a declaration of independence.

Another year—two at the most—and Texas would be ready. But Sam's words fell on deaf ears.

The settlers of Gonzales boasted a cannon for defense against Indians. A Mexican colonel decided to reclaim the weapon and sent a hundred dragoons to get it. Some hundred and fifty settlers loaded the cannon with chains and scrap iron. They devised a flag with the inscription COME AND TAKE IT! The Mexican dragoons fell back before its deadly discharge. One was killed.

Excited messengers spread the word to other settlements. Sam hesitated no longer. This skirmish must be built into the proportions of another Lexington. He sold his land for twenty-five thousand dollars and sent couriers racing to the United States with appeals for help. He sat up an entire night penning the letters.

"Volunteers from the United States will . . . receive liberal bounties of land. . . . Come with a good rifle and come soon. . . . Liberty or Death! . . . Down with the usurper!"

Nacogdoches seethed with action the next day. Sam had an early caller, Thomas J. Rusk.

"We're organizing a company of volunteers," Rusk said excitedly. "You'll lead it, of course."

Sam shook his head. "That's putting the cart before the horse," he advised. "Texas must organize a government first. Enrollment of companies can wait."

"Government can wait," insisted Rusk. "We're itching to fight, General."

"Whom will you fight?" asked Sam. "How about uniforms . . . cannons?"

Rusk shrugged his shoulders. "We don't need them. We'll stop to palaver after we've chased every Mexican out of Texas. There are plenty of men heading toward Bexar right now, General. If we don't hurry, we'll miss all the fun."

"You won't miss anything," protested Sam. "There are fifteen hundred Mexican regulars at Bexar. I know their commander—General Martin Cos. He is a competent military man. He has artillery and a store of ammunition.

Will you get anywhere attacking Bexar in bunches? Who will command these scattered voluntary companies?"

"You will," Rusk said quickly. "You're the only general in Texas."

"I will if I'm chosen," Sam said. "But I must be elected, Tom—*properly* elected. Right now Stephen Austin is commander-in-chief of any Texas military force. Do you want Austin to organize our revolutionary army?"

"He'll yield to you," Rusk said. "He is no commander. He's a great man, but no soldier!"

"I think he will yield, too. But in due order, Tom. Let's not run around like chickens with their heads chopped off. Get your company ready. Check each man's rifle and powder. There will be a call for some sort of meeting. There must be."

The messenger reached Nacogdoches the next day. Each settlement was to send delegates to a parley at San Felipe on October 16. This would be a "consultation." Delegates should come prepared to vote on independence.

Sam sighed and packed extra clothes into his saddlebags. Was there no restraining these hotheads! They had learned nothing from the early failures of the American Revolution. This time he wouldn't wait for other speakers to voice his sentiments. He intended to be among the first speakers heard at San Felipe.

★ 9

A Country of Chaos

THE DELEGATES WERE ALREADY DIVIDED IN THEIR OPINIONS. Wharton, Sam Carson, Martin Parmer, and Richard Ellis were clamoring for quick adjournment. Why palaver? Volunteers were marching on Bexar! Cut the gab short, elect Sam Houston commander and hustle along to the fighting! This was the majority sentiment.

Sam demurred. Some delegates weren't ready for such drastic action. Lorenzo de Zavala and Erasmo Seguin did not take kindly to bitter attacks on Mexico. Was their quarrel with a race of people or with the administration of Santa Anna? Others hesitated about removing Stephen F. Austin from military authority. True, he claimed no war experience except for casual campaigns against nondescript Indian clans. But he was still Austin, the great builder and dreamer.

Sam sensed the hesitancies. He had his own reasons for wanting delay. No help had come from the United States as yet, and wouldn't for months. Volunteers travel by horseback. War weapons must come in slow wagons or slow schooners. Adolphus Sterne had left Nacogdoches as soon as Sam. The merchant was en route to New Orleans to recruit men and solicit money. He meant to invest his own funds in this fight for freedom, and intended to provide a homespun uniform for every volunteer. Sam knew that other investors in Texas lands would be as generous. These landholdings were worth potential millions. And what would President Jackson do? All he could; Sam was sure of that.

But he couldn't declaim these things in public. De Zavala and Seguin would resent even an unofficial agreement with the United States. They wanted Santa Anna overthrown, and Texas to get full human rights; but they feared the ambitious United States. They would turn around and fight annexation of Texas as another United States territory.

So Sam chose his words carefully. "We are not land grabbers," he said. "We are not foot-loose adventurers. We are dedicated citizens of a province. We must hold to our cause. We must prevent haphazard bloodshed. There must be no fighting without formal organization. This consultation must organize its provisional government and name a provisional commander-in-chief. And we must frame our purpose for posterity. I move that we vote allegiance to the constitution of 1824, which guaranteed full and equal citizenship to all Mexican citizens. That is all we must have and that is all to which we are entitled."

De Zavala and Seguin voiced immediate approval. Sam had expected that. But his words were meant for other ears, too. The average Texan had no thought of international implications and would scoff at the idea of appeasing European powers. Sam knew that it was not too soon to make a play in that direction. Both Junius Booth and Daniel Webster, he felt, would approve—one of his poise and self-expression, the other of his statesmanlike reasoning.

Quick objection came. "The attack on Bexar is already the beginning," argued Grayson. "The war is already here. The men in the field are not waiting for us. They won't wait."

Sam sighed. That couldn't be denied.

"Before we proceed further," proposed Carson, "let us authorize General Houston to intervene at Bexar. If he can persuade the volunteers to hold their fire until we act, well and good. If he can't—"

Mr. Carson left his resolution unfinished. But his meaning was clear. If war could be delayed or avoided, well and good. If not, then cut short the talk and get on with the shooting.

Thirty delegates rode with Sam to Bexar. They found almost three hundred restless volunteers encamped on the Salado River. Austin held nominal command but Sam instantly recognized a challenging authority, Francis Johnson. Johnson wanted an immediate assault. So did Ben Milam, a rugged and colorful man who had failed as an *empresario* but was well liked by his fellow Americans.

General Martin Cos held Bexar with twelve hundred regular troops. The Mexican general was disturbed but confident. He had no orders to suppress these colonists but he intended to hold Bexar if attacked.

Sam appealed privately to Jim Bowie. The sandy-haired frontier fighter shrugged his shoulders.

"There's no calming 'em, Sam. They're fired up. They think they can lick the whole world."

"Cos will destroy them."

"Maybe; maybe not. The average Mexican hasn't much stomach for this war."

"And would have even less," Sam said quickly, "if we quit talking about independence and claimed only our rights as Mexican citizens."

"That's the truth," nodded Bowie. The Mexicans held

sacred the constitution of 1824, which had set forth all the high aims of the Mexican revolution. Santa Anna had ridden into power on the fervent feelings of dissatisfied patriots.

Sam's wasn't the only voice begging for delay. Other delegates rode to Bexar to argue for time and organization. The volunteer leaders finally consented to wait for Texans to organize a government and choose an official flag. The statesmen were in solemn session by November 3.

Hot words flew back and forth. William Wharton argued for immediate declaration of war and independence. Sam rose in buckskins to oppose such rashness. He put on soiled garments purposely, to show that the man expected to command the Texas armies didn't even possess a uniform. His unimpressive appearance shamed high-sounding talk. Their temporary treasurer, Gail Borden, emphasized the shaky position of this provisional government. It boasted a capital of just over sixty dollars.

Henry Smith was elected provisional governor. He was a "compromise choice," neither a warlike orator nor an "Austin conservative." The election of a commander-in-chief took less time. Sam Houston was named on the first ballot. Only one delegate dissented.

Commander-in-chief! Sam put aside the buckskins for a uniform tailored in New Orleans. Now all he needed was an army and artillery.

He had neither. The two volunteer groups in the field paid little attention to instructions from San Felipe. Stephen Austin surrendered command of the volunteers threatening Bexar. He went to the United States to beg loans, and Edward Burleson took over. James W. Fannin commanded a growing army at Goliad. But these were "minutemen," in the tradition of Lexington and Concord, not even militia. Sam hadn't forgotten the lesson of the Creek war. Decisive battles were won by organized troops.

He didn't believe, for instance, that the Texans could take Bexar without artillery; neither did Burleson, now a general. But the three hundred reckless riflemen charged the historic town in early December. A heroic gesture set them wild. Gray-haired, grizzled Ben Milam shook his fist at the Mexican lines and yelled out, "Who'll follow old Ben Milam into Bexar!" All three hundred did. General Cos surrendered on December 10. The victors paroled the captives and exulted in captured cannons and powder.

It was a glorious victory. More volunteers by-passed San Felipe, flocking to the triumphant leaders. Why bother with Sam Houston! Francis Johnson and Dr. James Grant, a Scottish soldier of fortune, were leaders more to their liking. Johnson and Grant called for more volunteers to march on Mexico. Texas was already won. So why not grab Coahuila and Tamaulipas, too? Annex all of northern Mexico while they were about it!

The first volunteer company arrived from the United States in Mr. Sterne's homespun suits—the New Orleans "Grays." They marched on to Bexar with Houston's orders to Colonel Joseph C. Neill, Burleson's successor: "Demolish the fortifications . . . remove all cannons . . . blow up the Alamo, and abandon Bexar. . . . I would come to supervise such arrangements myself but I must meet Colonel Ward's troop."

Ward was a Georgian who had brought a well-equipped battalion of volunteers to Texas. The company landed on the Gulf Coast and marched inland.

Sam, riding into Goliad, found alarming evidence that James Fannin meant to flout his authority. Proclamations called for more volunteers to invade Mexico.

"Troops shall be paid out of the first spoils taken from the enemy!"

Houston raged as he read that promise. He wanted no looting raids across the Rio Grande. He blazed out his suspicions of Dr. Grant, who claimed to own silver mines in Coahuila. Was Grant plotting for Texas or for recovery of his personal fortunes? How did Mexican liberals feel about this announced campaign to loot their native country?

The angry commander-in-chief rode on to Refugio. Colonel Ward and the Georgia volunteers were gone. So was Fannin, and there was not a pound of supplies in the town.

Sam was told the armies had marched southward. He overtook a company under Francis Johnson.

"You will turn back to Goliad at once, sir," Sam blazed.

"Not on your sweet life, General," Johnson said calmly. "I take my orders from Fannin—nobody else. And we're riding for the Rio Grande."

"As commander-in-chief I order you—"

"Who says you're the top dog?" drawled the colonel. "The talk I hear is that you've been booted out. You and Henry Smith, too."

"Your information is based on dastardly lies."

"I reckon not. You've been gallivanting around the country and ducking out of the fighting. You never showed up at Bexar. You scoot on back to San Felipe, General, and you'll find I'm right. Smith is out as governor. Fannin is bossing field operations."

Sam studied Johnson. There was no doubting that this newly appointed colonel believed he spoke the truth. And it might well be true. Henry Smith had been a compromise choice. Not even his backers considered him strong enough to hold authority long. The delegates had been in a hurry to organize some sort of provisional government—in too much of a hurry.

"I would like permission to address the troops," growled Sam.

"Sure," agreed Johnson. "You won't get anywhere, though. This bunch won't stop this side of Matamoras."

Johnson was right. The volunteers listened respectfully for a time, then showed impatience. They weren't about to turn back, they said. They must beat Grant's force to Matamoras—Fannin's, too. They meant to grab a full share of the spoils, not to settle for leftovers.

"Men, you are invading a nation!" appealed Sam. "Mexico is divided now, torn by dissension. Why do you think Cos capitulated at Bexar? His troops were ready to rebel against him. Their actual sympathies lay with us. But to invade Mexico—that's to unite all Mexican factions behind Santa Anna. Don't talk to me of conquering fortifications. Can you level forts with your squirrel rifles?"

"We'll give 'em a fit, General," grinned a lanky sergeant. "You high monkety-monks didn't think we could take Bexar. You tried to talk us out of it."

Sam threw up his hands. There was nothing to do but pull aside and let the army resume its march.

He rode slowly back to San Felipe. Was this his fate—to be rejected as commander before he had a chance to prove his metal? Was this beginning of a great revolution to become another grabbing adventure? He groaned, thinking of the international complications. Andrew Jackson must disavow all concern for such marches to Matamoras. Great Britain and France would lose no time in demanding such action. Were Grant and Johnson and Fannin so ignorant of world affairs? Didn't they realize that both England and France would send help to crush any threat to Mexico?

Governor Smith gave partial confirmation of Johnson's story. The majority wanted him out, Smith ruefully admitted. They were clamoring for another meeting. Austin was off in the United States. "I wouldn't last two minutes without his active backing," said the governor.

Probably he wouldn't either, thought Sam. He couldn't help smiling at the irony of the situation. He had seen Austin's influence as a challenge to his ambitions for Texas. He had been a silent partner to the election of William Wharton as chairman of the first consultation. Now Sam prayed for Austin's early return from the United States.

Sam walked to the window and stared out miserably. "There is nothing for me to do here," he said. "I can't lend my name to piratical war. And our troops have degenerated to that, Governor—pirates."

"I have sent instructions to the field that you are to be obeyed," Smith said hopelessly. "Is there more we can do?"

"Yes," said Sam, turning in sudden decision. "You can give me a leave of absence. You can order me to contact Indian tribes. We need their neutrality if not their help."

"And that would get you off the griddle for a couple of months," speculated Smith.

"Exactly. I can't tolerate my present plight, Governor. I hold a nominal command only—not a single command accepting my orders. I don't want any bit of responsibility for what happens to Johnson, Grant or Fannin. I want it well known in the United States that Houston has washed his hands of such looting expeditions."

He gestured with both hands. "When I have returned, and Austin has returned, perhaps Texans will listen to reason—and we can do something about building a country."

Henry Smith's eyes twinkled. "You'd leave me to face the music, General?"

"Is there anything else to do?"

"No," Smith said slowly. He sighed. "I was wounded at Velasco, General. I've carried the scar for three years. Another one won't hurt. You go deal with Indians. I'll take care of things. I'll dissolve the council. The chief executive can do that in times of emergency, and I'm not out as governor yet. Then we'll see—what we shall see."

★ 10

The Runaway Scrape

THE WOODS PROVED A TONIC. SAM TOOK HIS TIME ALONG the wilderness trails, avoiding white men whenever possible. He killed game for food and camped in sheltering thickets, often in wet and chill. He longed for reports from the battle fronts but avoided inquiry. He had accepted a command, then had been stripped of all authority. The next time he would leave no doubts as to the conditions of his acceptance. Did Texas want Sam Houston commanding its armies or traveling obscure trails alone—as a self-appointed emissary to Indians? He would give Grant, Johnson and Fannin the rope to hang themselves.

His longest visit was with a segment of the Cherokee Nation living near Nacogdoches. These red men were kinsmen of Oo-loo-te-ka's people. They welcomed Co-lon-neh warmly, but Chief Bowl refused to talk of alliance with white men.

"Ay," he said bitterly, "we fought once. Yi, by the river, by the Tallapoosa. Co-lon-neh was there. We swam the river and took away the canoes of the Creeks. The Red Sticks were under the charm of the Messiah, Tecumseh. But not us. We served the White Father and destroyed the Red Sticks, the greatest of all Indian fighters. And what did the White Father do for us? Yi, what did he do? He herded us together like sheep and scattered us west of the Great River—in the West, where death and dishonor awaits the red men. *Hayee,* it is true. Co-lon-neh has never broken his word. This is your lodge and my people are your people. *Toen,* it is true. But we do not march with the white man again."

Sam nodded, disturbed by the ancient Indian's bitterness. The Bowl was almost eighty, even more venerable than Oo-loo-te-ka. *Hayee,* he whispered, the Bowl spoke truth. Co-lon-neh's people had misused him. Sam remembered Tennessee and Washington—the political scheming of Billy Carroll, the dedicated nationalism of Andrew Jackson. The flag must march westward. The Mississippi was the first great goal, then the broad-stretching Louisiana territory. Now what? Texas, for sure. Sam's eyes saddened. Even Co-lon-neh was not all these trusting Indians believed. Co-lon-neh had become another Jackson, seizing all things in his rough hands, molding them into his pattern.

He whittled busily on a pine sliver. The Bowl watched curiously, wondering what his visitor wanted to design. The Cherokee had never seen Washington. He didn't recognize the outline of the national capitol.

"The Mexicans have used you poorly, too," Sam pointed out. "You have lived here twelve years without getting title to your lands. You tried to help them, too. You would not join the rebellion against them. You killed Richard Field and John Dunn Hunter because they signed treaties with the white men."

"*Toen,*" nodded the Bowl. "And I would be slain in my sleep, too. My warriors fight with you, Co-lon-neh."

"Will they stay out of the war?"

"Ay," promised the old chief. "Yi, we will do more. We will ask the gods to favor Co-lon-neh."

Sam rode on. He meant to show positive proof of his success when next he met with Texas political bigwigs. He would show his responsibility met. What would be the report from Refugio and Matamoras and San Patricio?

A bitter wet norther forced him to seek shelter at Anahuac. The home of George Hockley was his choice.

"Lordee, General," exclaimed his host, "they have been looking everywhere for you! There's talk the Indians scalped you. There's big doings set for Washington-on-the-Brazos next week. The council is finally rid of Henry Smith. James Robinson is acting governor and that doesn't suit at all. There's talk you might even be president—if people could find you."

Sam disclaimed such an idea. "That can wait," he said firmly. "I could not sit and doodle with papers while there is a war to be won. I must do something for Texas. If I can't command an army, I must do what I can. The Cherokees won't help the Mexicans. Neither will the Tonkawas or the Caddos." He hesitated. "You can promise my presence at Washington," he added. "I will be there at the appointed hour and give a full report of my activities. I am sorry to hear about Governor Smith. Texas has lost a good man."

Perhaps a better man than he, Sam reflected as he rode on his way. Henry Smith had stayed at San Felipe to face the repercussions. Johnson and Grant were not available. They had stripped Bexar of captured war materials and led off stout volunteers on fools' errands. Now Texans were aroused to these early follies. Their fury fell on Governor Smith, not their nominal military leader. Sam had made it plain that he was in no way responsible.

He cut a notch on his cane for each passing day. He

started for Washington-on-the-Brazos in late February. Who had insisted that the delegates meet there instead of at San Felipe? It was a shrewd step, showing charged feeling about Austin's cautious leadership and arousing sympathy in the United States at the same time. What American wouldn't thrill to the news that Texans had proclaimed their independence at a place called Washington!

Sam reached the village a day earlier than he had expected; he had forgotten that it was leap year. Washington was four years old. It boasted two small inns and some hundred cabins. The meeting would be held in a blacksmith's shop.

The delegates, without rooms or shelter, milled about the settlement streets. Their garments were soaked with cold drizzle, but they scorned the weather. The first news was heartening. Austin and the other commissioner to the United States had borrowed two hundred thousand dollars. The second report was entirely different. Santa Anna had crossed the Rio Grande with a sizable army.

Then came a spent horse staggering in with a weary rider. His message was so vital that the delegates assembled a day early. It was from William Barret Travis. It was read in a hushed voice:

"BEXAR, February 24, 1836

"TO THE PEOPLE OF TEXAS AND ALL AMERICANS IN THE WORLD:

"I am besieged by a thousand or more Mexicans under Santa Anna. I have sustained a continual bombardment and cannonade for 24 hours and have not lost a man. The enemy has demanded a surrender at discretion; otherwise, the garrison will be put to the sword . . . if the fort is taken. I have answered the demand with a cannon shot and our flag still waves proudly from the wall. *I shall never surrender or retreat.* Then, I call on you, in the name of Liberty, of patriotism and everything dear to our American character, to come to our aid with all dispatch. The enemy is receiving reinforcements daily and no doubt will increase to three or four thousand in four or five days. If this is neglected, I am determined to sustain myself as long as possible . . . VICTORY OR DEATH." . . .

Who was William Barrett Travis? Delegates who knew explained excitedly. He was a South Carolina lawyer who had been a ringleader in the 1832 demonstration. He had led twenty-five volunteers to Bexar a few weeks before. Why should he be in command at the Alamo? Where was Bowie?

Voices thundered; talk spread. Sam learned what had happened during his solitary mission. Davy Crockett had come to fight for Texas—"Colonel" Crockett, with a handful of Tennesseeans. Supposedly they had gone to defend the Alamo. Colonel Neill had yielded command because of illness. Less than two hundred men were arrayed against all of Santa Anna's might.

Robert Potter, another Carolinian, leaped to his feet. How could they dally here and play with words while fellow Texans were in danger? He moved that they adjourn at once and every man march to the relief of the surrounded mission.

Vigorous assent came from all corners of the cheerless room.

Sam rose quickly. He had intended to make no speech before this assembly, but he saw the happenings of San Felipe again. They had postponed the organization of government there because of concern about Bexar. What had happened? The Texans had taken Bexar but had failed to gain everything from the victory. A close friend and a fine man, Henry Smith, had been sacrificed on a political altar.

"We are here to form a government," he said gravely. "We have gathered from all corners of Texas to perform a specific mission. We were not sent here to form still another volunteer company."

He hesitated. What should he say about the authority of the commander-in-chief? He decided to plunge ahead.

"You elected me once as your commander," he said boldly. "You gave me the title but not the authority. You elevated me to an exalted position but left the actual command of each company to its captain. Confusion has resulted, bleak defeat. I propose that we organize our government and choose an actual commander. Let us profit from the experiences of George Washington in the American Revolution. It isn't necessary to weigh my personal feelings. Name another to lead your armies, if you will. I shall only give him my blessing and ride from this place to serve in the ranks. But, be it as general or as private, let me serve an organized government. Let me fight for a cause and a country."

The impatient delegates subsided. Richard Ellis pounded with his gavel.

"I hereby appoint a committee to draft a declaration of independence," he announced. "We will convene here tomorrow and hear its report."

Sam regretted a day's delay but supposed it couldn't be helped. He heard with approval that George Childress was one of the men named to draft a declaration. George was a fellow Tennesseean and a former Jackson follower. It pleased Sam even more when he learned that Childress had come prepared for just such a responsibility. He had a completed draft to show his fellow committeemen.

The next day was Sam's forty-third birthday. He dressed fittingly; at least differently. He went to the convention wearing Cherokee coat and buckskin vest, high-heeled boots with silver spurs, and a soft-brimmed hat.

Childress' declaration gained quick approval. It was voted to send the original copy to the State Department at Washington and distribute other copies among the leading Texas settlements. Then the delegates considered an ad interim government.

Sam squirmed as David Burnet was nominated acting president, but he decided against any expression of opposition. It wouldn't do for the acting commander-in-chief to take a strong voice in civil government. Sam considered Lorenzo de Zavala an excellent choice for vice-president. Now there would be no doubt about the loyalty of the Mexican-born patriots.

Sam sat uncomfortably through another long session, then rose for his second speech.

The delegates now must consider the details of government organization, he said, and he was delighted at their intense concentration. But the Texas commander-in-chief should be in the field, organizing volunteers, not debating civil issues. If the gentlemen would sustain him in his authority, he would leave at once for the battle front.

The vote was quick and overwhelming.

"Thank you, gentlemen," Sam said slowly. "I will give you cause to long remember this authority you have conferred. I pray that you will never regret it."

He bowed and left the smithy's shop. Couriers from Bexar had brought revised estimates of Santa Anna's strength. The Mexican dictator had crossed the Rio

Grande with seven thousand regulars. Any march to Travis' rescue was out of the question.

Not all men agreed. Captain Moseley Baker did not. "Do you mean, General," he demanded, "that we should loiter here and leave the Alamo to its fate?"

By "here" he meant Gonzales. Baker had recruited three hundred and seventy-five volunteers, intending to join Francis Johnson's march toward Matamoras. Sam had intercepted the company at Gonzales and had countermanded Baker's orders immediately. There would be no more of this chasing here and there for Texas troops, with each commander acting on his own. The first order of business, declared the general, was to organize these rugged individualists into an army. Baker's company would do as a nucleus.

Sam shocked Captain Baker by putting his ear to the ground and listening intently. The fighting was over at the Alamo, he said grimly. He heard no more reverberations in the earth.

"General, it's ninety miles to the Alamo," protested Baker. "You can't be sure." The captain put his ear to the damp soil and heard nothing.

"You forget, Captain," smiled Sam, "that I have abilities taught by the Indians."

"Are we white men," demanded Baker, "or do we make war like Indians? Are you a general or a medicine man?"

"Do not flout orders, Captain Baker," Sam snapped. "I was voted supreme command at Washington-on-the-Brazos. Don't put that authority to the test."

Years before, pursuing the Creeks, Old Hickory had sentenced a militiaman to be shot. Jackson had gotten nowhere with discipline until it was done. Sam hoped he could avoid such a drastic example. Moseley Baker listened tight-lipped. None of his men would be shot for insubordination, he promised, without the prior execution of their captain.

"That could be ordered if necessary," Sam said coldly.

He sent a courier to Fannin. Abandon Goliad at once, read the orders, and join the main force at Harrisburg. The orders included Colonel Ward's volunteers from Georgia, self-styled "Red Rovers" because of their colorful uniforms.

Sam took personal charge of drills. Baker's sullen volunteers formed into uneven lines. They marched and countermarched for a long day. They were sore and weary that night, but not too tired to protest against night watches.

"I cannot promise, General," Baker said stiffly, "how long my men will endure such treatment."

Sam's eyes gleamed. He was tired, too. But he considered that the recruits had acquitted themselves well during their first day of drilling. He said so.

"As for their spirits," he added calmly, "let them know the truth. The training will get harder instead of easier."

Two more volunteer companies reached Gonzales, and two hundred more disgusted volunteers found themselves sweating in the warm March sun. Sam's hopes rose as the ranks spread wider. Five hundred men now and Fannin expected any day! A dispatch from President Burnet promised fieldpieces from the United States. Such cannons would not arrive soon enough. Sam disbanded Baker's detail of gunners. In a campaign the two small pieces at Gonzales would be more trouble than they were worth.

Every day brought discouraging reports from the second Mexican army, commanded by General Vicente

Filisola. The Mexican strategy was simple to understand. The two forces would unite somewhere near San Felipe or Harrisburg and sweep to the Sabine as one army.

Could either force be stopped, much less both? The general rolled in his blanket but could not sleep. He could hope for three thousand men and artillery by May. It would be that long before Texas was ready for war. And he was not doing things a commander-in-chief should. He should have scouts to Santa Anna's rear, cutting off more supplies from Mexico. Horsemen moving around the enemy's rear—if he could wish such a cavalry force into action!

Drilling halted abruptly the next morning. A small bedraggled party reached Gonzales, and their tragic story spread like wildfire. An unkempt but still attractive young woman trembled as she described the massacre at the Alamo.

She was Angelina Dickinson. She caressed a fifteen-month-old child while a Negro slave watched solicitously. Her dress was stained with the blood of Alamo defenders. She had watched them fall one by one, her husband included. Santa Anna hadn't spared a man. Even Jim Bowie, helpless with chills and fever, had been riddled with bayonets. Davy Crockett had been the last defender. He had finally dropped with the victims piled high around him.

Sam's eyes looked off for an instant. So Davy Crockett, one of Old Hickory's choices for political greatness, was already dead! And all those brave defenders of the Alamo wiped out in a senseless battle for power.

Santa Anna had spared Mrs. Dickinson to carry his grim message to all Texas rebels. Death for those who didn't lay down their arms immediately!

Sam had expected such word from Bexar. He was

resigned to it, but he hadn't counted on the effect upon Texas morale. The news created sheer panic. The inhabitants of Gonzales collected personal belongings and begged the return of wagons conscripted for army use. The general assembled his eight hundred volunteers—that many now.

"There are almost eight hundred of us and we will fight in the open, not behind a wall," he declared. "We will scatter into the timber if necessary and fight as our fathers did at Kings Mountain. We can stand off an army ten times our size. No military force in the world can destroy Americans armed with long rifles. Have you forgotten New Orleans so soon?"

It was a brave speech. It soothed the volunteers. Then came another chilling report—striking as a bolt from the blue.

Goliad!

Fannin had surrendered to the other Mexican army. The Texans had accepted promises of honorable treatment as prisoners of war. Instead Santa Anna had ordered their immediate massacre. The Texans were marched out of the Goliad mission in their regular companies and shot down. No orderly, formal execution—just wanton shooting. A handful survived by diving into the San Antonio River and swimming to safety. But the rest were dead, including nearly all of the Red Rovers from Georgia.

Sam stalked away so that his rage wouldn't be a public spectacle. Orders from President Burnet did nothing to soothe him.

The President and his cabinet were retiring to Galveston Island to avoid capture. It was necessary to put miles of bay water between themselves and the invaders.

But Burnet had other plans for Sam Houston and his ragged army.

Don't be cowards, urged the President. Relieve the country of its panic. Stand and fight. Engage the enemy at once.

★ 11

The Last Retreat

STAND AND FIGHT! SAM FINALLY REGAINED CONTROL OF his temper. Formal parade counted only a few more than seven hundred in his ranks. How could he be sure from one day to the next, the way volunteers slipped off into the night? Fifty men reached camp on March 31, but half their number turned right around and marched back home. If all was lost, then they had better see about getting their families out of Texas!

Was all lost? Sam kept his own grim counsel. He ordered Gonzales abandoned, and struggled with fleeing civilians along the Atascosita road.

Another official message came from Burnet: "Sir, the enemy are laughing you to scorn. You must stand and fight."

Fight, railed Sam to himself. They couldn't even effect an orderly retreat, with the entire population of Texas swelling the roads. He had no cannons now, and no powder. His ranks were growing. His was the only Texas army now; Santa Anna, Filisola and Urrea had gobbled up the others.

Sam ordered a count of his troops on April 2 and thirteen hundred responded. But this was a surface unity only. Moseley Baker hadn't forgotten the sharp words exchanged at Gonzales. A new arrival from Kentucky,

Sidney Sherman, encountered the same harsh discipline and didn't like it. Colonel Sherman boasted a well-armed company and also a battle flag—a banner of white silk embroidered with an amateurish figure of the goddess Liberty. Sam heard rumors of the secret coalition involving several of his captains.

They were ready to kick Houston out and turn the command over to Sherman. But they waited for some sort of official recognition from President Burnet.

Sam brooded over this insubordination, then took action. Ordering two graves dug, he formed ranks around them and issued a grim warning. He hoped the cavities would not be filled with dead deserters.

The Brazos was no easy stream to cross, not even for an army with so little paraphernalia, but by April 15 the Texas army was marching east of the muddy river. Santa Anna's army pressed close behind—crossing the Brazos next day, some thirty miles upstream. The Mexican dictator burned one Texas settlement after another. Urrea and Filisola were moving inland from the coast.

The secret coalition of disgusted officers held another meeting. If something wasn't done soon, it would be too late. Their stern general refused to discuss his plans with anyone. If they must judge by appearances, then they would guess that he meant to retreat all the way to the Sabine River, the southwestern boundary of the United States.

He would never do it, vowed one of his colonels. He would be assassinated in his blankets first. Not far ahead was a road junction. One route led on to Nacogdoches; the other turned south. If the madman kept going east, they would strike! Their honor required it.

The "madman" heard of their plan. His eyes gleamed but he didn't bother to search out the plotters. A wagon rolled into camp that night and Sam was shaken out of sound sleep.

It contained powder from Galveston and cannons—two new fieldpieces, iron six-pounders bought by champions of Texas liberty in Ohio. Sam caressed their cold barrels.

"Just alike," he murmured. "Just like sisters, twin sisters."

He sent an orderly through the camp arousing men who possessed blacksmith skills. They set to work before daylight cutting up old horseshoes for ammunition. Sam supervised them closely. He could use a hammer and heat a forge as well as any man, and he wanted these iron fragments small enough to scatter.

Sam studied a frayed map by flickering firelight and then assigned a scout company to ride around Santa Anna's flanks. He could have reassured some of his officers, but he didn't. Let them fret over which road he would take. He knew. He had artillery and scouts. It would be up to Deaf Smith's men to see that the Mexicans had no route of retreat.

My, wasn't he the bold one, planning the destruction of a force stronger and better armed than his own! Sam's eyes twinkled as he formed other plans. He ordered a crossing of Buffalo Bayou. Nearby cabins were looted to build makeshift rafts. His order took the army by surprise.

Back across the bayou! And why destroy their rafts afterward? The rebellious officers held secret counsel and decided to wait their time. At least the army hadn't taken the Nacogdoches road.

Deaf's couriers galloped up as the weary Texans were cooking their first meal in two days. Their tidings spread before the general could stop them. Santa Anna's army was heading for Lynch's Ferry, only a few miles downstream.

Texan spirits rose to overflowing. They had been dead wrong about their hulking grim commander. Sidney Sherman and Moseley Baker swapped surprised looks and hurried about their duties with subdued expressions. The maneuvering made sense now. Santa Anna's army had penetrated the swampy region around the lower bayou. The Texans held all the advantage of any battle position.

General Houston ordered ranks formed with the first sign of daylight. No breakfast either; he seemed to know just where to lead them and to be in a hurry to get there. His choice of position found quick favor. Thick great oaks screened their formation. The two cannons commanded a stretch of open prairie. Santa Anna, moving toward the junction of Buffalo Bayou and the San Jacinto River, could not avoid them.

But there was more waiting. The Mexicans came on slowly. Finally a dotted line of skirmishers showed on the savanna. Minutes later the Texans sighted parallel columns of infantry and cavalry. The slender lances of Santa Anna's dragoons threw shimmering reflections into the thick timber. A commotion in the brush startled the bug-eyed men squatting behind the oaks—Deaf Smith's scouts reporting again. The bridge over Vince's Bayou had been destroyed. There was no retreat from this battlefield for Santa Anna, the self-styled Napoleon of the West.

Sam rode slowly from one position to the next. "Make your first shot count," he told Joe Neill, commanding the "Twin Sisters."

"We'll mow 'em down, General," promised Neill.

The Mexicans were halting four hundred yards from

the Texas lines. Sam sensed their uncertainty. Did the oaks screen a sizable force or only a Texas patrol? The general spurred his white stallion into a brisk trot.

"Hold your fire, men," he begged his infantry. A new leader, Mirabeau B. Lamar, who had earned quick promotion from private to colonel, waited impatiently to hurl the cavalry into furious charge.

Sam squinted into the afternoon sun. The Mexicans were stringing together a barricade of pack saddles and camp paraphernalia. His lips twitched. Could such flimsy breastworks hold his Texans? He looked along his eager lines and knew they couldn't.

"Hold your fire, men."

His order was relayed from man to man, finally to Neill's gunners.

Sam signaled with his hat. A blast of assorted iron raked the skimpy Mexican breastworks. The hail of sudden death threw the dragoons into panic. Lamar's fifty cavalrymen burst out of the oaks and charged at a gallop. Eerie yells sounded from a thousand parched throats. Here came the infantry in head-on assault, muskets belching fire, then bowie knives flashing in the bright sun.

From the edge of the woods came faint music. A drummer and a fifer struggled with a lone song, "Come to the Bower." The strains were barely audible. The shouts of inspired men rose over all sound, including the roaring cannon.

"Remember the Alamo! Remember Goliad!"

Sam felt the white stallion sink under him. He leaped clear, pitching forward on his face. He was wounded, for searing pain numbed his ankle. He tried to struggle up, dropped again. A hand caught his shoulder as a young Texas cavalryman helped him rise and mount a scrawny pony. The big stallion lay dead. Sam Houston would not ride to glory on a white horse.

But ride on he did, with his pulse beating wildly against his temples. Smoke churned in angry billows. There was no way of surveying the whole battle scene. The general must be satisfied with fleeting glimpses. Here a tangle of men fought, another formed.

There was no doubting the battle's tide. The enemy was scattering everywhere, gray-clad men fleeing in all directions. A bullet thudded into Sam's pony and he scrambled down. The mount was only hit, not killed. Sam looked around him and caught the bridle of a riderless horse. He suddenly realized his right boot was filled with blood. But it was no time to fret about another wound. This was victory more glorious than he had dared to anticipate.

Only one unit of the Mexican army held together, Juan Almonte's cavalry. Sam spurred his horse forward when he saw that Almonte wanted to surrender. The Mexican officer expressed no fear, only resignation. His troop was led off to watch the rest of the battle quietly.

Or was it a battle? Sam reeled in the saddle and struggled to see more clearly. He saw carnage everywhere he looked. The Mexican resistance had collapsed in a few minutes.

Sam fought to make himself heard above the din. "Remember this is civilized war. Accept honorable surrender. We do not slaughter prisoners."

Few heard him. The Texans were hot in pursuit. Rifle butts thudded and bowies flashed. Sam heard Mexican soldiers plead for mercy. "Me no Alamo, me no Goliad!" The denials swelled into a thin, pitiful chant. Many were being slashed down anyhow. Sam shouted to Sherman, Lamar, Baker. "Stop the slaughter."

Then suddenly he reined up his borrowed pony. Everything was swimming before him. He reeled in the saddle and reached out to stop the closest officer.

"Help me down," Sam begged. George Hockley leaped to the ground and reached up to assist the general. Sam slipped downward and collapsed.

The sun was setting when Sam regained consciousness. He lay with half-closed eyes, silent, until he became aware of his surroundings. He lay underneath one of the oaks which had screened the size of his army. Skilled hands were probing his wound. Sam sighed. He knew the surgeon's last name, Ewing. The physician had joined the ranks as a volunteer. He seemed to know his business.

"What are . . . the . . . men doing?" Sam asked.

Dr. Ewing chuckled. "Splendid, General. Santa Anna's army is finished. There is nothing left but to chase down stragglers."

"Are the officers in charge?" Sam asked anxiously. "Are they keeping order?"

"Very well, considering everything," said Ewing.

Sam struggled until he was propped against the tree trunk. "Is my wound serious?"

"Yes, General, quite serious. There is a shattered bone. Am I hurting you?"

Sam gritted his teeth. "Of course you are hurting me," he snapped. "But don't stop for that. Where is Hockley?"

"He could be found. But is it absolutely necessary, General? The battle is won. Can't you forget responsibility and let me treat this ankle?"

"I must see Hockley. He must write a dispatch to Jackson."

"President Jackson!"

"Yes. Fetch Hockley. Tell him to find paper and pen somehow."

Sam turned on his side and gestured to Deaf Smith. "Pick out your best rider. Mount him on a fast horse."

"Can't the message wait?" said Dr. Ewing.

"No," Sam said firmly. "There has been too much waiting already."

The note was penciled and Deaf's scout galloped toward Nacogdoches. Sam lay back and formed a mental picture of the communication's flight eastward. Post messengers would surely carry on the word. Sam groaned as Dr. Ewing probed his wound again. He shut his eyes tight. Forget the pain, think of the sweet. Think of a weary rider reaching Nashville at last, croaking the news as he turned over his missive to another horseman. The Texans have conquered Santa Anna! How would history recognize the battle? Sam flinched and set his teeth against the torturous probing of Dr. Ewing's instruments. He must compose another report, an announcement to David Burnet. This time Sam would explain that he had conquered the enemy at San Jacinto.

The victorious general lapsed into a coma, He slept fitfully throughout the night, awakening with dawn. His head cleared quickly as a prisoner was brought forward. The slight Mexican wore a blue cotton smock and felt slippers, but there was dignity in his voice as he announced his identity.

"I am General Antonio López de Santa Anna, President of Mexico, commander-in-chief of the army of operations. I place myself at the disposal of the brave General Houston."

Sam forced himself to one elbow. "General Santa

Anna!" No man had reported any evidence of the Mexican commander until this morning. "Ah, indeed—I am glad to see you."

What did one say to such a prisoner, the president and dictator of a nation! Lorenzo de Zavala came forward to act as interpreter. Sam managed a smile in spite of his pain. The battle had been fought a short distance from Zavala's newly built home! What a moment of triumph for the Mexican patriot who had helped rouse Texas to revolution! Zavala had fled Mexico to escape Santa Anna's personal persecution. Now Lorenzo carefully relayed the words of the two commanders back and forth.

"The man who conquers the Napoleon of the West is born to no common destiny," Santa Anna said smoothly. "It now remains for him to be generous to the vanquished."

Sam shook his head. He had given no thought to what would be done with a captured president. How had Santa Anna managed to avoid massacre?

"You should have remembered that at the Alamo," Sam said grimly. "What excuse do you offer for the massacre of Fannin's men?"

Santa Anna lifted a nervous hand to his pale face. A ring of hostile Texans had formed around them. Mutters rose at Sam's question. Santa Anna's proud composure deserted him. He trembled and spoke to Zavala in an undertone. He must have opium, he begged, sinking to the ground. Let them bring his baggage.

Cold-eyed men brought the Mexican's luggage. He fumbled in a leather case until he found his medicine. He sat on the ground until calmed by the drug. Then he could continue.

He proposed an armistice. Sam shook his head. Not

unless the terms applied to Filisola and Urrea also. Santa Anna immediately penned orders to his other generals. The war was over—for the time being, at least.

It would have been ended for Sam Houston anyhow. Dr. Ewing despaired of picking out all the bone segments with his crude instruments. He ordered the wounded man to New Orleans at once.

Sam demurred.

"You could die, man," Dr. Ewing said sharply. "And you have too much to live for."

That sobered him. He had a lot to live for indeed. The dependable Hockley hurried about making arrangements. The master of a trading schooner consented to take on a passenger and Sam was carried aboard on a litter.

But victory's sweetness was tainted at once. Confusion and discord showed in the victorious camp as David Burnet arrived from Galveston Island and voiced dissatisfaction with the armistice agreement. The President conferred with Santa Anna behind closed doors.

Burnet showed no hesitation about granting Houston a leave of absence. In fact, the acting president appointed another commander-in-chief in a matter of minutes. Mirabeau B. Lamar was elevated to the position. Houston's lips twitched. From private to commanding general in two short weeks! Lamar, a young Georgian with a flair for poetic language, couldn't be accused of timidity. He wasn't Sam's choice, but President Burnet didn't bother to consult with him.

More volunteers arrived from the United States—too late for the war but in time to wrangle about the spoils of victory. Tom Rusk, Hockley and Stephen Austin brought reports to the suffering general. He listened closely despite his great pain. Texas events, he reflected bitterly, were taking on a familiar human pattern. Politicians were rushing in, now that the last shots had been fired.

"We have five thousand idle men on our hands," Rusk despaired. "We don't need them, but we don't dare turn them loose to hustle for themselves. Already they are talking about grants of land."

Sam appealed to Austin to persuade Burnet and Lamar to act slowly. There was more to establishing a republic than winning a battle. Austin promised to do his best.

Sam's eyes gleamed as he stared across the waters of Galveston Bay. He must bide his time once more, call again on the patience taught him by the Cherokees. He must lie quietly until his ankle mended. But Burnet and Lamar and Sherman—what did they take him for? Did they know so little about the mettle of the man they tried to undermine? Did they actually believe that Sam Houston was sailing off into oblivion? Had they forgotten that he had learned politics from Andrew Jackson, as well as military leadership? Sam's lips formed a cold smile. David Burnet was ad interim President of Texas, nothing more. And that, whispered the prostrate man, was all that Burnet would ever be.

★ 12

Texas Is Rebuffed

THE *Flora* ROLLED IN A GULF STORM FOR SEVEN DAYS before reaching New Orleans. Sam was in agony every moment. He lay in a stupor as the small schooner finally docked. The commotion roused him, for he had chosen to stay on deck because of the stifling heat. Struggling to his feet, he leaned on makeshift crutches.

The wharves were jammed with cheering spectators. New Orleans deserved a better appearance. The Crescent City had sent the first United States volunteer company, the "Grays," to Texas. They had died at the Alamo or with Johnson and Grant. Not a few of this excited populace felt that a personal score was settled.

Sam stood there a sad sight, and knew it. His coat was tattered; he had no hat; his stained and stinking shirt was wound about the shattered ankle. A man in beaver hat and bright-colored cravat sprang to his side, and Sam leaned on his shoulder. If it hadn't been for this man, William Christy, the hero of the hour would never have made it up the gangplank. Sam stumbled once, crossing the wharf, and fell against a wide-eyed young lady who had pressed close in her excitement. He focused his wild eyes upon her.

"I am very sorry, Miss," he said hoarsely. "I am very sorry."

Somehow her voice sounded clear despite the din.

"You mustn't be sorry, General Houston. I am thrilled that I kept you from falling."

With Mr. Christy's help Sam staggered on, but he looked back over his shoulder. "Who is she?" he asked the merchant. "Have I ever met her? Her face seems strangely familiar."

"We won't worry about that now," Mr. Christy said firmly. "You must get to a doctor."

A litter was waiting. Sam collapsed on it and was carried away. He felt himself being lifted onto a soft bed with a high canopy. Solicitous hands bathed his face and body, stripped away his ragged clothes. Then he realized that three surgeons were laboring over his ankle. By dark they had removed twenty bone fragments. Sam wanted to rail out against their pessimistic predictions but couldn't muster the strength. He had been nearer death after Horseshoe Bend. He had survived days in the southern swamps and had recovered despite casual treatment by inexpert army doctors. Now he had the best of medical attention and personal care. He had no intention of dying.

By morning his doctors agreed with him. He was a hardy man, they said happily, but he would be bedbound for some time.

By the third day Sam was demanding that Christy inform him about Texas happenings. The merchant evaded the first questions, then finally told all he knew. Aroused Texans had tried to execute Santa Anna. They had dragged him from a prison ship in iron manacles, but calmer reason had finally prevailed. The dictator was at present confined at a Brazos River plantation. Arrangements were being made to return him to his native country via the United States.

Other reports had been printed in the New Orleans newspapers. The United States was all agog over the victory. A dispatch from Texas was more eagerly read than any news from Washington.

The Texas army had refused to accept Lamar as commander-in-chief. A friend of Mr. Christy supplied the details by letter. David Burnet had been stunned by this insubordination. He had tried to enforce his authority and had looked ridiculous. Finally Thomas Rusk had taken charge of the military forces. A smile touched Sam's face. Rusk could be trusted.

Every day brought more accounts of growing unrest and confusion in the new republic. The convention at Washington-on-the-Brazos had authored a constitution along with its declaration of independence. But the convention's clerk had carried all of the copies with him to Tennessee. Where was the document? A Nashville newspaper had printed it *in toto*. So had a Cincinnati journal.

"I have a copy," said Mr. Christy. "At least I suppose it is an exact copy. I have sent another copy to Gail Borden at Harrisburg. I am sure he will publish it in his newspaper."

Sam nodded. Borden would. He recalled that Borden had sunk his press in the Brazos River before Santa Anna captured San Felipe.

Sam read the constitution closely. It was an adequate document, he decided. The delegates had framed it after he had ridden off to take personal command of Baker's company. He noted that the constitution provided for immediate election of regular officers once peace had been won.

Well, it was won now. Sam sat up.

"I must go back," he said, "and at once."

"You aren't fit for travel," Mr. Christy objected.

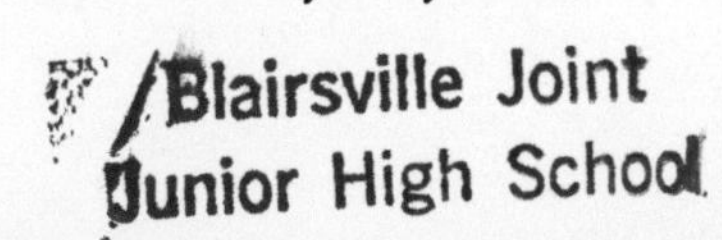

"I must return anyhow," Sam declared. "My ankle can mend as well on horseback as in this bed. We need to call an early election. Texas will collapse under provisional authorities."

The merchant sighed. He had invested heavily in Texas lands; he couldn't deny the urgency of the situation. "You are sorely needed, all right," he said. "You must offer yourself for president, General."

Sam nodded. Had he intended anything else?

Mr. Christy persuaded him to rest two days longer. Sam read the newspapers eagerly. The future of Texas was already a bitter political topic in the United States. Eastern editors accused Andrew Jackson and Sam Houston of having completed a land-grabbing scheme. Unable to acquire Texas by honorable purchase, they charged, President Jackson had sent his personal emissary to take charge of the adventurers. The bugaboo of slavery was already a part of the talk.

"It won't be easy to gain annexation," mused Mr. Christy. "The abolitionists will fight it tooth and toenail. So will most of the Whigs. And any such treaty would have to be approved by two-thirds of the Senate."

"It will not be easy," agreed Sam. "But we will find a way. No group of isolationists can stop our westward march."

The general suddenly remembered something which had bothered him often during these idle days. "That young lady I fell against—did you learn anything about her?"

Mr. Christy's eyes twinkled. "Yes. She is Miss Margaret Lea of Alabama. She was visiting relatives in the city. I conveyed your apologies to her. She was most gracious. She said no offense was taken and that she was praying for your speedy and complete recovery."

Sam was disappointed. He had hoped she was a New Orleans resident.

"Has she—returned to Alabama?"

"Yes. Two days ago."

"Would it be presumptuous to write her a note of apology?"

The merchant smiled. "I think she would be the most thrilled young lady in the South." Mr. Christy rose. "But you make too much of a trivial incident, General. The young lady understands that you were weak and delirious. I'll see about a horse for you, and a more suitable wardrobe." He studied the patient an instant before adding, "You know what awaits you in Texas, of course?"

Sam nodded. "I know," he said slowly. "The presidency. The problems of organizing a government. The uncertainties of our relations with the United States. The risk of new invasion by Mexico. The cat-and-mouse games with European monarchs. And the Comanche Indians—they are more of a menace than you realize."

"No doubt," agreed Mr. Christy. "I do not envy you, General. Are you strong enough for the ordeal?"

"No," Sam said honestly and humbly. "No man is. But assure our friends in the United States that I shall do my best."

Sam watched the parade of voters to the polls. A cheer swept the crowded street as the latest tally was announced. Three cheers for old Sam! A happy group of grizzled men headed for the saloon across the street to drink that toast.

He was confident of the outcome. The main thing, he recalled, had been to get Burnet to set an election date. How the man had stalled, offering this excuse and then another! His hesitancy had cost him whatever chance he might ever have had of being a candidate himself. Sam had found two factions already campaigning. Henry Smith still had loyal backers and, of course, Stephen F. Austin's name was mentioned everywhere, but neither campaigned against Sam. The election was considered only a formality.

The ballot contained two proposals for the electorate to consider—the constitution as reprinted in Mr. Borden's newspaper and a resolution providing for immediate annexation to the United States.

Mid-afternoon brought preliminary reports from Anahuac and Harrisburg and Velasco. Houston was leading by a topheavy margin. Both proposals were carrying almost unanimously. The constitution suited Texas voters and nearly every ballot registered approval of annexation.

The final count showed 5119 for Sam to 743 for Smith and 587 for Austin.

Sam Houston took the oath of office on October 22, 1836, at 4:00 P.M. in the temporary capital, Columbia. By nightfall the new Chief Executive was attacking the duties of his office. He wrote until his fingers ached and dawn seeped through the single window of his small office. The only furnishings were a plain pine table and a cane-bottomed chair. An engraved cuff link removed from his own shirt served as a seal of office.

He was pleased with his beginning, especially when three secretaries reported for work the next day. Commissions and messages went out at a furious pace.

"In the name of the Republic of Texas, Free, Sovereign and Independent . . . to all to whom these Presents shall come or in anywise concern: I, Sam Houston, President thereof, send greetings." . . .

The most important commission went to William H.

Wharton, minister plenipotentiary to the United States, with instructions to obtain recognition of both Texas independence and annexation.

Most other matters could wait, especially those dealing with appropriations and awards of public lands. The new republic boasted some two hundred and fifty million acres of public domain. Only one-tenth of its area was covered by titles issued under Spanish and Mexican regimes. Speculators clamored for the land to be parceled out. The President delayed the signing of legislation creating a Texas land office. The open lands must go to settlers, not speculators.

Official word came from Wharton, traveling eastward: "The leading newspapers of the North and East oppose annexation on the old grounds of . . . extension of slavery and fear of southern preponderance in the councils of the Nation." . . .

Sam's lips twitched. He had expected that. The Whig party would fight annexation every inch of the way. But Andrew Jackson still held forth in the White House. The dream of Texas had belonged to Jackson in the first place —as far as Sam was concerned. As a youth he had ridden southward at Old Hickory's suggestion.

Days passed. Finally came Wharton's first dispatch from the Potomac: "I regret to say that I have been unable to secure an audience with President Jackson. I am informed that he is ill much of the time and barely able to draft his next message to Congress. But I have been assured by his closest friends that his message will recommend recognition and Congress will approve with a minimum of debate."

Stephen F. Austin was the first other man to read Wharton's report. He had accepted the appointment as Secretary of State and had attacked these duties with the same fervor with which he had launched his colonies. Sam's respect for the slight, rather timid man grew by leaps and bound. Austin was no great leader and never would be, but his capacity for work was unbelievable. And he doted on details, which the President was too apt to put aside.

Austin's features turned even paler. "We must get recognition at least," he said anxiously, "and no later than next March. We will be lost without it."

Sam shook his head and brought out his jackknife. He was suddenly gloomy about Wharton's prospects of immediate success. Other letters from Washington warned of Jackson's failing health. Sam could imagine the confusion without Old Hickory's firm hands on the reins. He remembered well the political alliance between New York and the West. Why not? He had arranged it himself. It was understood that Martin Van Buren would follow Jackson as the acknowledged leader of the alliance. Sam sighed. He himself had arranged that order of succession. The West would back Van Buren in '36 if New York would support Jackson in '28. Van Buren wasn't greatly concerned about Texas.

Austin fell ill. Sam visited the Secretary of State on December 27, and found him delirious.

"Texas is recognized!" he cried out as Sam entered. "Didn't you read it in the papers?"

Sam pretended he had. But it hadn't happened and he was more worried than he would admit.

Austin died that afternoon. Sam dictated a sad announcement: "The father of Texas is no more. General Stephen F. Austin, Secretary of State, expired this day."

A few days later came the startling text of President Jackson's message to Congress.

Sam was bewildered as he read and reread the chilling words: "Recognition [of Texas] at this time . . . would scarcely be regarded with that prudent reserve with which he have hitherto held ourselves bound to treat all similar questions!"

A hoarse sob came from Sam's throat. "Prudent reserve"! Could Andrew Jackson have chosen those words himself? Jackson, who had conquered the Creeks, who had driven back the Seminoles and opened up Florida to white settlers, who had sacrificed the Cherokees on his altar of westward expansion, who had sent his favorite lieutenant to investigate unrest south of the Sabine!

But no matter who had framed the phrase, Jackson was the speaker. Texas must flounder along without the blessing of its mother country. Sam's jackknife sliced away on a pine sliver. Could any republic exist without official recognition of its neighbors? No trade relays, no diplomatic correspondence, no mail exchange, no help against invaders! Sam brooded a long while, then snapped shut his knife.

He had underestimated Whig strength. He hadn't believed any political group could curb Jackson's ambition to carry the flag westward. But the Whigs had done it—they and the abolitionists and the New Yorkers weary of Tennessee's political supremacy.

But, resolved Houston, there were other ways to skin a cat. The American tune would change if Texas grew strong and prosperous. Let the Lone Star nation show its mettle and establish close relations with Great Britain and France.

Sam spoke to the alarmed people as he had addressed his ragged army at Gonzales.

Texas offered land—great areas of land. Some men

were eager to invest fortunes in its development. So far they had gotten no encouragement from the new government. But the President welcomed foreign investors now, especially those who meant to improve Texas harbors. Take the Allen brothers, John and William. They were building a city on Buffalo Bayou, near where the historic battle had been fought. They wanted to name their town Houston and locate the Texas seat of government there.

Why not? Sam's ties with the old life grew easier and easier to forget. He forced himself to shrug aside melancholy thoughts. He must face it; he no longer wore Jackson's colors into western arenas. He was no lieutenant, but a full-fledged leader himself.

And why grieve for the widening breach with old associates? Was there real happiness to sacrifice? Not for him. He was forty-four years old and more alone than ever.

He dashed off a proud message to Wharton, cautioning the minister to hold himself aloof from newspapers and congressmen.

"Texas must come into the Union as a bride arrayed for the altar, not as a humble suppliant."

Next he attacked the neglected papers on his unvarnished table. Buried in the mass of documents was an unopened letter. Its contents brought his first smile in several days. Margaret Lea's girlish handwriting was easy to read.

"I am overwhelmed by your thoughtfulness. . . . With all your responsibilities, you found time to apologize for something so trivial. . . . I shall pray for your long life and your success as President of Texas."

Official matters waited as the President of Texas stared at the letter in his hand. She was very young; he remembered that much about her. And, in social ways, Sam had never been young or frivolous. He had been too old and formal for Eliza. It was folly to dream again.

But weren't dreams the only antidote for loneliness?

★ 13

Co-lo-neh Woos a Maid

THE TEXAS CONSTITUTION PROHIBITED CONSECUTIVE TERMS for any president. Sam Houston must yield the reins for three years. He remembered Billy Carroll's mistake and did not try to handpick his successor. He considered two of the three candidates acceptable. Both James Collingsworth and Peter Grayson were capable, conservative statesmen.

The third aspirant—well, Sam tried not to think about Lamar, nor the candidate for vice-president, Burnet. The feeling was mutual as far as the latter was concerned. Burnet usually referred to the outgoing president as a "half-Indian." Sam retaliated by calling Burnet a "hog thief."

Lamar appeared to have little chance of election. Most of his backing came from Texans who opposed annexation. Then politics took an eerie turn. Both Collingsworth and Grayson committed suicide during the campaign. Lamar won by default, and there was nothing for Sam to do but accept his successor. Sam did that with the best grace he could manage, and with both private and public prayers for the nation's survival in the trying times ahead.

Lamar was the most ambitious dreamer anywhere. His inaugural address included all of his wild promises. He boasted that Texas would not consider annexation even if it were offered. He proposed to expand the Texas boundaries to the Pacific Ocean and subdue all Indian tribes in the West. He announced plans to divert the Santa Fe trade to Texas ports. He declared intentions of organizing a navy which would control all gulf waters, including those off Mexico. And he quickly launched the construction of a new capital city, a town built on the glorious precedent of Washington, D.C. The new capital would be named Austin after the "real" father of Texas!

Sam expected nothing good from this new regime. Lamar's extravagant ideas made the actual facts of Texas' progress seem trivial. Texas had moved forward in her first three years of constitutional government. The Lone Star nation was recognized by most European powers as well as by the United States. But the Texas treasury was empty. Its population was new and couldn't pay heavy taxes. Federal improvements, such as proposed roads to the Red River and a fleet of ships, cost money. Texas had none.

Neither did its outgoing president, for that matter. But Sam Houston, lawyer and shrewd adviser about Texas investments, could take immediate steps to improve his personal circumstances.

He had three years to make money for himself and pursue a notion he had confided to no one. Several communities offered to honor him as a congressman, but Sam meant to leave politics alone. The carping critic was never popular. Let Lamar hang himself with his own rope. Sam would wait until the strained Texas situation recalled him to authority.

He owned land, many acres of it. He carried powers of attorney for friends who owned several times as much. The crying need of Texas communities was capital. It wasn't available in Texas, but Houston knew his political and military success would impress businessmen and investors in the United States.

However, his role as a private citizen deceived no one, not even himself. The independence of Texas was a goad to southern political leaders. The South wanted new slaveholding states to strengthen its congressional bloc. Van Buren, though a Democrat, wanted no more expansion of slave territory. The Democrats meant to offer a presidential candidate pledged to the annexation to Texas.

So Sam found it politically expedient to visit Mississippi and Georgia and Alabama—to point out financial opportunities in Texas, to encourage immigration, to confer with political leaders.

Such a route, of course, led to Alabama. There, at a strawberry festival staged by Mr. and Mrs. William Bledsoe, Sam formally met Margaret Lea.

He bowed very low. "I am charmed," he said gently.

"I am honored," answered Margaret.

He studied her closely. He hadn't realized her hair was so dark. It was chestnut brown except for a gay band of golden ringlets around her temples. She was slim and held herself with quiet dignity, but the tranquillity of her eyes and features made the biggest impression. Here, sensed Sam, was a young woman who would never be disturbed by trifles. How he envied that! He ignored most small things, but others affected him out of proportion. The small things were still his pitfalls.

"I have never forgotten your shocked expression when I stumbled against you," Sam reminded her.

"I know," said Margaret. "It caused you to inquire about me and to make an unnecessary apology."

Her clear eyes looked off, then came back. "It was silly of me to press so close," she confessed. "Unladylike, too. I had heard you were wounded. Still I was shocked to see you so weak and helpless." Her lips formed a quick smile. "I suppose I thought the hero of San Jacinto could span the dock with one leap."

"I have never fought a battle without suffering a severe wound," Sam said slowly. "That is true in peace as well as in war," he added.

"But you win your campaigns . . . eventually?"

"Do I? I often wonder." He spoke his honest thoughts. Could he consider himself a successful man? Fame, he knew, was not the same as success.

"Haven't you won Texas?"

"Not yet," he smiled. "Mexico still intends to reconquer us, if Santa Anna can ever muster the strength. And Texas isn't in the Union. In fact, we are further from it than before San Jacinto." He thought about Lamar's extravagant schemes. "The present Texas administration doesn't even want annexation. Mr. Lamar wants to go it alone. There were other Texas republics. Their founders either lost their heads or died in prison."

"How many others?"

"Two at least, not counting a small uprising in Nacogdoches. One of our soldiers at San Jacinto had fought for two other republics."

"I didn't realize that," Margaret said slowly. Her eyes swept across his face. "You must tell me more about Texas, General Houston. I am very interested."

"About what Texas is—or what Texas can be?"

"About what Texas *shall* be," Margaret said firmly. "My mother will be interested, too. She is considering selling out here and buying land across the Sabine."

Houston's heart beat quicker. He had not dared hope for that. Then they did have a mutual interest.

"Your mother is a widow?"

"Yes, but don't pity her on that account. She is a shrewd investor." Margaret looked around, but her mother was nowhere in sight. "She intends to confer with you. You will talk to her?"

"Of course." Sam was happy to oblige.

He told Mrs. Lea and Margaret about the river bottoms which would yield a bale of cotton per acre. He described the low-lying prairies converging on Bexar, where cattle and mustangs ran wild. The first American adventurers had gone to Texas to capture wild horses. The Texas revolutionaries had eaten wild beef both before and after San Jacinto. Farther west, he explained, grass grew hip-high and buffalo fed by the thousands. This was Indian country, the Comanche hunting grounds—and Indians such as the South had never seen: half-naked warriors on speedy, shaggy ponies who thought nothing of riding three hundred miles to attack a foe.

Margaret Lea was fascinated. Her mother's interest was shrewder and entirely impersonal. How was cotton moved to market, by river traffic or through the timber? How did slaves fare in the climate? How many cotton gins were operating?

Sam sighed. Margaret had spoken truthfully; Mrs. Lea was a shrewd woman.

He answered as best he could, but their talk left him with some misgivings. Margaret Lea might be dazzled by a hero's stature, but not her mother. Nancy Lea was concerned only with practical matters.

Sam traveled on, grappling with his own impetuous nature. Once before he had swept an impressionable girl off her feet. The resulting wound still brought painful flashes, though Eliza had obtained a divorce and married again. This time Sam must be sure. He could offer much to a young woman but not all of it was stately glamour. He couldn't deny that he was a lonely, moody man in turns, and possessed of tempers and plagued by inconsistencies. A young woman of Nacogdoches had told him frankly that he was a poor matrimonial risk.

Sam sent no couriers scurrying back to Alabama with flowery messages. Whatever he wanted to know about Margaret he would find out for himself, and in his own good time.

Besides, there was other business. His route took him finally to Nashville. Andrew Jackson sat with a shawl around his bony shoulders and offered no apology for the rebuff of 1836. Nor would he guarantee what lay ahead.

"It isn't simple to annex another country," mused Jackson. "It has never been done before. The process must begin with a treaty. Two-thirds of the Senate must ratify any such agreement. When have we ever been blessed with such a majority?"

That was true, of course.

"And there are your debts," continued the strong man of the Democratic party. "They must be paid. John Quincy Adams brings up those debts every time Texas is mentioned in Congress. Who would pay those obligations if Texas were annexed? Our New England senators are often penny-wise and pound-foolish."

"Then let Texas retain her public lands and face her own debts," proposed Houston.

"How long can you hold on to your public lands? They are given out free to encourage settlement. Roads must be built at public expense. The citizens of established communities resent paying for such roads. They can't realize that turnpikes profit the entire country. The United States could never have managed solvency without the turnpike over the mountains."

Sam nodded. The national highway had linked West and East. Eastern taxpapers had screamed about its high costs, but the turnpike had brought trade between the frontier and the established cities. Except for that turnpike, and Spanish shenanigans on the Mississippi River, the United States might never have become an economic unit.

Jackson seemed weary. "Oh, annexation will come," he promised. "But it won't be easy. The abolitionists put the slavery issue ahead of anything else. Our coalition with New York is on shaky ground. We can dominate the House, but not the Senate. We are gaining in the House. That makes the Whigs all the more determined to block the admission of a new state. Texas would give us two more votes in the Senate."

Sam took out his jackknife. It wasn't true that Jackson had lost his political faculties. He could still talk cold turkey to a man he trusted.

"Texas must wait out a political development, too," Houston said, and briefly described Lamar's policies. "I am afraid that we are in for a financial panic."

Jackson smiled. "It was such a panic that took us to Washington. Remember?"

Sam remembered well. He hadn't forgotten, either, how he had dealt with early Texas chaos in 1836. Then he had left the scene on the excuse of treating with the Cherokees. Now he was attending to personal business.

Lamar's schemes made news in the United States. The Texas navy was helping Mexican revolutionists in the province of Yucatán. An expedition was going to cross the unsettled West and open trade with New Mexico. The New Orleans *Picayune* had a gifted writer assigned to Texas, James Wilkins Kendall, who apparently thought well of the Texas president.

Sam digested every news account of such ventures. He opposed public expenditures for such promotions, especially when Lamar ordered the Santa Fe expedition on presidential authority alone. These schemes didn't threaten the independence of Texas, but that fantastic proposal, the Franco-Texienne bill, certainly did!

Sam read of it in the *Picayune* and decided to hurry back. The scheme was outrageous. France had sent a diplomat to Texas named Alphonse de Saligny. De Saligny proposed that France lend five million dollars to the hard-pressed republic and that French troops garrison twenty-five fortresses in Texas. In return, French emigrants would get huge tracts of the public domain lying along the principal rivers.

It was one thing to flaunt closer relations with Europe in the face of reluctant American congressmen. Only such a threat would overcome opposition to the annexation of more slaveholding territory. But to accept military protection from a European power— Was Lamar insane! Did he want to bring on a future war between America and France?

Sam couldn't resist a detour. Nancy Lea's talk of investing in Texas lands wasn't idle female chatter. William Bledsoe was toying with the idea, too. Sam's arguments convinced both. Finally they left him alone with Margaret.

"I must ask a question," he said slowly. "It is an honest question and I must have an answer."

She nodded.

"I am near forty-seven years of age," Sam pointed out. "In doing many things I have been all kinds of a man. You have heard I have lived among the Indians, and that is true. You know that I have rashly thrown away great opportunities. That is true, too. Had I not complicated my own life, with my own impetuous ways, I would now be in line for the Democratic presidential nomination. I have made money and have lost it. I arrived in Texas eight years ago without a dollar in my pockets. I am old to be trying again for personal and domestic happiness. But I think that the first time I saw you—even as delirious as I was—I knew I must try again."

Margaret's head was bent low. She was listening closely—he was sure of that—but she gave no hint of her reaction.

"I must return to Texas at once," Sam went on. "I had not intended to take part in any legislative wrangles of this administration. But the future of Texas, of the United States and of this hemisphere demands that the Franco-Texienne bill be blocked. I cannot linger here to pay court in the usual manner. I would prove a most unconventional suitor if I did. The usual ways of society aren't mine and never were. I cannot ask a young lady's hand as it should be done. I can only reach out for it—rather crudely—and hope that she does not pull away."

He made no move. He had spoken. He waited for her answer.

Margaret's head came up slowly. Her lips trembled as she faced him. She glanced at his arms, held rigid against his body.

"You do not reach very far, General," she chided.

"You mean . . ."

"I haven't stirred," she said with a faint smile.

"No," he said hoarsely, "and if I do reach . . . if I do

touch you once, if I take this forward step, then I shall never step back—nor shall you ever get away."

"Yes, General," she said meekly, but with a flash of her gray eyes.

Now to face another barrier, Nancy Lea. The widow's lips went tight, but she didn't bother to pretend surprise.

"I was unwilling to believe it," she said. "I suppose there was no avoiding it. Margaret is determined to share the rest of your life. She has high hopes for both you and herself."

"I will move heaven and earth to see that she is not disappointed," promised Sam.

Nancy Lea shook her head. "Heaven and earth do not make a happy marriage," she said a little dryly. "Only a man and a woman can do that."

She tossed her graying head. "You are not my idea of a perfect son-in-law, General," she said directly. "But there seems to be nothing I can do about it. I won't object, therefore. But I must ask about your plans. You say you must return to Texas at once. When will you come back for your bride?"

Sam hesitated. He hadn't allowed himself to plan that far ahead.

"It is imperative that I return," he thought aloud. "This French alliance must be prevented. Yet we mustn't offend France. I suppose the thing to do is to copy the Whig strategy and bottle up the bill in the Senate. Then I must begin my campaign for another term. Any doubts I ever had about running again are gone. I am needed."

"Yes," nodded Mrs. Lea, "you are needed." Her eyes twinkled. "As a prospective landowner in Texas, I endorse you for the presidency. And without reservations."

Sam nodded his appreciation. "You are coming to

Texas, you and Mr. Bledsoe. Couldn't Margaret come with you—and the wedding be held in Galveston, or Houston?"

He waited hopefully. Could any man ask more than to be married in the city named for him?

"No," Nancy Lea said firmly. "My daughter will be married in her own home. The man who gets her for a wife will find time to return for her."

Sam laughed softly. He would return.

★ 14

Texas Plays a Lone Game

THE DAY WAS MAY 9, 1840. VIOLINS PLAYED SOFTLY AS the bright-eyed bride descended the stairs. Sam waited nervously. Had any woman ever looked so lovely? Finally her small, trembling hand lay in his and they heard the minister's words with bowed heads.

Then it was over, the reception as well as the ceremony. Nancy Lea had required that the wedding be held in Alabama, but Sam had balked at any lengthy stay there. The journey back to Texas must serve as a honeymoon. Business interests as well as politics required his early return.

A house was waiting to receive them, a rented structure in Huntsville. Sam's eyes twinkled as he recalled Nancy Lea's questions about accommodations for her daughter.

"I understand," the widow said sharply, "that you have been living in a one-room hut in Austin. And sleeping on a dirt floor."

Sam chuckled. So he had, for a few weeks—to show up the extravagances of the Lamar administration. "That was just politics," he explained. "I have rented a comfortable house."

Nancy nodded, then brought up another rumor. "Did

you receive that French count naked, crouched on a table, gnawing a bone?"

"No," Sam said instantly. He sighed. "You hear all sorts of things about Houston. No story is entirely correct. I am not as bad as some make me out, nor as heroic as others claim." A smile spread slowly across his features. "There is always a motive for my unusual conduct. I wanted to stall action on that Franco-Texienne bill. I didn't want Texas borrowing five million dollars, nor France holding a monopoly along our choice rivers. We must face our future as an independent nation."

"Then you despair of annexation?"

"I didn't say that, ma'am. We must prepare ourselves for independent existence. It's been four years since San Jacinto. We are no nearer to statehood. But we are even nearer to bankruptcy as a nation. That's why I must get back to Texas. I must win this election. The crisis demands it."

"Yes," conceded Mrs. Lea, "you must succeed Lamar." Her eyes twinkled. "I am your ardent political supporter. It's just natural that I worry about my daughter's future."

"I am resolved to put her happiness before anything else," Sam declared.

He meant that. Many of his political backers believed the marriage a grave mistake. Dr. Ashbel Smith had warned him of the possible repercussions. "If this marriage fails," he had said, "you are finished as a public figure. No man can survive two scandals."

Sam knew that the doctor was right. He realized what he was risking. But what were fame and physical comforts without happiness? He must rid himself of this haunting feeling that he walked alone even in a crowd. It would be no easy struggle; he realized that. He had no doubt either about his most dangerous enemy, himself. He must set his will to it as he had struggled to live after the Creek war.

The carriage moved briskly. Stops were brief. Sam must install his wife in the rented Huntsville house and travel on to Austin. He would not take Margaret to the new capital on the Colorado. Its only inns catered chiefly to whisky-drinking guests. Its society was often violent. Duels were fought every few days. The "affair of honor" between two high-ranking generals shocked Margaret when she heard talk about it.

"That is barbarism!" she said disgustedly. "You must promise, Sam. No duels for you."

He chuckled. This was one fault he had settled years ago. "I have been challenged a dozen times," he told her. "I would receive challenges daily even if it weren't well known how I feel about them."

He briefly described the only duel he had ever fought. "I suffered unmitigated torment until General White recovered. I have never been tempted since to accept pistols or swords."

"How do you answer when you are charged with cowardice?"

Sam showed her. He threw open his shirt, exposing his naked chest. "These are the scars of one war," he said. "I walk a little stiffly because of a second wound. I have fought and bled for both of my countries. Any man who wants to call me a coward is welcome."

A new political crisis arrived every day, but Sam held aloof from politics until a home was finished. He had promised to put his marriage ahead of political ambition and he kept his word. Nancy Lea, reaching Texas that autumn, found her daughter living in a roomy, two-story house which dominated a rolling East Texas plantation.

Slaves were busy clearing fields. Sam would be the region's biggest planter the next spring.

He would also be the next President of Texas. Mirabeau Lamar shifted more and more responsibilities to Vice-President Burnet. Sam's attacks on the administration took a bitter turn. Burnet was the "little man" who had ordered a battle against Santa Anna before the army acquired either cannon or powder. This was the politician who had rushed to the battlefield to take over the arrangements of victory. Sam was not pleased when Burnet announced his own candidacy. Sam had accepted election the first time, speaking well of his two opponents at every turn, drawing both into his cabinet. But he and Burnet—this was a fight to political death!

Every event played into Sam's hands. The Texas currency fell to three cents on the dollar. The expedition to Santa Fe ended in disaster. Count de Saligny fell out with an Austin innkeeper and left the capital, vowing never to return.

Sam Houston crushed Burnet under an avalanche of ballots.

"You aren't—taking me to Austin?"

Margaret could put off the question no longer. It had shocked her to realize that he meant to go alone to his second inauguration as president. She had looked forward to sharing the honors and to converting the presidential mansion into a temporary home. But Sam's plans for the next congressional session did not include her! Instead, he was hurrying to complete a new home on the gulf shore. Margaret suffered from seasonal attacks of asthma; he hoped the gulf climate would benefit her.

"No," Sam said. He gave sound reasons. The presidential house leaked. Lamar, a bachelor, had taken poor care of the Texas "White House." Austin was still hit by occasional Indian attacks. Three persons had been scalped near the capital in recent months. Living costs were high. All merchandise must be hauled in wagons over muddy, often impassable roads. Mail service was undependable. Another Mexican invasion was rumored and Austin was only three days' march from Bexar.

"Besides these things," explained Sam, "this will be an unhappy year of government. I must take actions which will turn public opinion against me. I will show a side that you know nothing about, except from gossip."

Margaret's eyes softened. She knew exactly what he meant. Sam was a different person with her and in his own home. His struggles were obvious, which made her appreciate them more. He was tender, considerate and even subdued. He belied every story about him, past or present. But away from his wife, in the political arena, he was still Sam Houston, voicing scorn for his enemies, rousing his supporters to new heights of enthusiasm.

Sam played gently with his wife's hair. "You might not approve of what I say and do in Austin," he said lightly. "And I might allow your disapprovals to temper my judgments and my actions. I intend this to be a brief session, lasting only the winter. I propose to get done what has to be done, then hurry home."

The incoming president chose a wardrobe to fit the tenor of his second inaugural address. He faced his listeners in buckskin shirt and trousers.

The Texas debt had reached twelve million dollars by that December 13, 1841. The treasury was receiving only $33,500 a month in taxes, and that in Texas money. At the rate of world exchange the revenues of the Lone Star nation weren't enough to pay even the president's salary.

"We have arrived at a crisis," Sam declared. "Our situation is worse than on the day after San Jacinto. We have done nothing except pace in circles since April 22, 1836. We have heeded idle dreamers and wasted glorious opportunities. We have danced, and now we must pay the fiddlers."

He ordered drastic cuts in appropriations, including his own salary. He ordered the seat of government moved temporarily to Washington-on-the-Brazos. He recalled the Texas navy from Mexican waters and stopped the pay of its officers and crews.

Then Sam slipped away from the Colorado to sit out the pending storm.

Outraged protests came from all Texas. Was Houston so small a man that he meant to destroy the capital named after Stephen F. Austin? Scrapping the navy, mustering out all military units except one spy company! Wasn't that inviting Santa Anna to take over? Had Sam Houston taken the presidency for the sole purpose of destroying Texas? Did he mean to starve out those Texans who had decided against annexation and wanted a bigger, stronger Texas?

The target of these attacks offered small comfort to his troubled wife. "I am afraid," he said gloomily, whittling away on a pine slab, "that things will get worse before they get better."

Newspaper editorials demanded that Sam explain his motives. The pressures mounted as a Mexican army crossed the Rio Grande and captured San Antonio without opposition. The spy company was there, but what could forty men do against two thousand? Aroused volunteers streamed toward Bexar and drove back the Mexicans. Then public opinion forced President Houston to order an army to advance as far as the Rio Grande.

He halted them there with instructions that the volunteers be marched back to Gonzales and disbanded. Some four hundred Texans refused to obey. They stormed Mier under the leadership of Colonel Dick Fisher and were captured by a force five times their number. The survivors drew black beans in a grim lottery for life and death. Every tenth Texan was executed and the others marched off to prison near Mexico City.

Congress thundered for the President to do something about the imprisoned men. Houston declined, except to request that France and Great Britain intervene in their behalf. Shades of Johnson and Grant, of Travis and Fannin! Why had four hundred supposedly strong and able Texans decided they could conquer Mexico without artillery or war supplies? They hadn't crossed the Rio Grande as a Texas army, but as adventurers. The President deplored their plight but he intended no retaliation. Call him traitor and coward again, he said wearily. He was inured to both invectives.

A year brought changes. Texas repeated a great harvest in 1843. Santa Anna, plagued with money troubles himself, sent no more armies north. Lone Star currency rose in value. Commerce between New Orleans and the Texas seaports brought rising profits.

Living conditions even improved at Washington-on-the-Brazos, though the Senate still met over a saloon. Sam allowed the government to rent the first family a house, and Margaret quickly converted the dwelling into a comfortable home. She brought carpets and upholstered furniture to the temporary capital, even a mahogany piano. Her playing delighted her husband, especially when she played "Come to the Bower." Why had the Texans chosen that for a battle aria at San Jacinto? Sam never knew himself.

He clung to one frontier custom—shaving every morning on the uncovered back porch without using a mirror. That habit led to unusual talks in the early hours of daylight. A frequent visitor was the latest British envoy to Texas, Captain Charles Elliott, who rose early and walked briskly before breakfast. Elliott had served his country in the Orient and wasn't disturbed at unusual settings for diplomatic conversation.

On this morning in August, 1843, Captain Elliott showed concern about a disturbing report that had been published in the last New Orleans *Picayune* to reach Texas. Was it true? Had President John Tyler offered to reopen the question of annexation?

Sam nodded. Mr. Tyler had indeed.

Elliott took a deep breath. How could this man be so casual about so important an international topic? England had sent the captain to Texas for two purposes—to arrange peace between Mexico and its former province and to prevent Texas from joining the Union.

"Is it amiss to ask . . . how you have replied?"

"Not at all," Sam said affably. "Mr. Tyler speaks for his office and himself. As President he can negotiate treaties with foreign powers. But the United States Senate must ratify all international agreements. I am not sure that the Senate would approve any such pact."

Elliott's features brightened. So English agents in Washington reported to London. He was glad to learn that Houston accepted the situation so calmly. Tyler's offer amounted to nothing more than the paper it was written on. But Elliott couldn't be satisfied with such simple answers. Who could be sure of President Houston's feeling for the United States? It was hard to forget that he was a native American and a former follower of Andrew Jackson.

"I have answered Mr. Tyler that Texas cannot commit herself at this time," Sam went on. "If we agreed to such a treaty, we would lose the friendship of England and Texas—"

"Of a certainty," murmured Elliott. "We couldn't do otherwise."

"And Texas would be out on a limb," finished Houston.

"Quite true," said Elliott.

His blue eyes twinkled as he relit his pipe. He had come to Texas sharing De Saligny's opinion of the Lone Star situation. Texas was an unsettled wilderness with an uncouth backwoodsman as president. But Captain Elliott no longer thought that. He ruefully reported to London that President Houston was nothing short of a diplomatic genius. He could be neither threatened nor swept into an alliance.

Now it was England's turn to be grilled. "Of course," Sam said, "we are bothered about the lack of news from Mexico. Will Santa Anna ever accept peace? If we knew that, we could be more certain about future relations with the United States."

Elliott's lips twitched. Both Great Britain and France were exerting pressure on Mexico, he explained. Neither country would lend more money to Santa Anna for military purposes. The campaign of 1842 had failed for lack of funds. Mexico wasn't improving its financial affairs, either. While Texas was paying off debts and building up commerce, Santa Anna was allowing his domestic affairs to get worse and worse.

There wouldn't be another invasion of Texas soon. Captain Elliott could promise that if Santa Anna wouldn't. The Mexican dictator still refused to consider proposals of armistice; but give them time, promised the Englishman. Great Britain and France could finally bring the dictator around. Chances were that he couldn't hold his office much longer without European help.

Sam nodded. He had risked the success of his administration on those chances.

"I shall advise our Foreign Office," promised Elliott, "that immediate action on an armistice is advisable."

The Englishman strolled away. Sam attacked the day's mail from the United States. A note from the State Department contained a sharp paragraph.

"Annexation would fail in the Senate," wrote Mr. Upshur. "And you must realize, sir, that this country will never allow another power to menace our position on this continent."

Sam scowled. Had any nation ever faced such a predicament? The United States would not take Texas; a vigorous minority checked every such move. But why doubt that the Union would go to war against a neighboring country which bid strongly for domination of the North American continent? Texas must be developed and must have European help to do it. But Texas mustn't grow too rapidly, and must not take too much help.

How long could Sam Houston play both ends against the middle? He picked up a letter from the aging Andrew Jackson.

The former President wrote in a shaky scrawl: "You know, my dear General, that I am putting down the slanders of British intrigue against you . . . you could never become the dupe to England, and all the gold of Santa Anna . . . could not seduce you from a just sense of duty and patriotism."

Sam carefully put the letter among his personal effects. The message both angered and saddened him. Old

Hickory seemed to have forgotten the cold rebuff to Texas in 1836. Then political expediency had required the United States President to act and speak cautiously. Probably it hadn't been his personal choice, but Jackson himself had delayed recognition of the new republic for a full year. Now, Sam mused with a thin smile, the shoe was on the other foot.

He took up his quill pen and answered Jackson's letter: "Our situation is peculiar. I am duty-bound not to take any action which would jeopardize the future of my country. Texas could exist without the United States, but the United States cannot, without great hazard, exist without Texas."

He signed the letter with a flourish, then began an answer to Secretary Upshur. Margaret broke in on its composition.

"Sam, aren't you ever coming to breakfast? Your grits are already cold."

"No matter," he said pleasantly. "Even cold grits are preferable to parched corn. I have had that for breakfast more than once."

He put his arm around his wife's waist. Those who believed him so enigmatic, he reflected, were omitting obvious factors from their human equations. Captain Charles Elliott suspected him of secret leanings toward the United States. Andy Jackson wondered if the onetime Tennesseean was not tainted by too friendly association with the British.

Neither was true. The fact was that Sam had found happiness and full contentment in Texas. Little dreams could be lost inside a big one. All other loyalties meant little compared to his new responsibility. Texas meant home and family.

What man wouldn't bargain sharply for such a stake!

★ 15

The "Squeeze Play"

TRUCE WAS REACHED WITH MEXICO. NOW PRESIDENT Houston could assign the Texas spy company to warfare against the Comanche Indians. This frontier fighting force was already acquiring world-wide fame as the Texas Rangers.

Every Texas event added to concern in the United States. The Lone Star republic granted colonization contracts similar to the *empresario* system formerly used by Mexico. A French Alsatian, Henri Castro, located some thousand families southwest of Bexar. An even more grandiose venture, the German Emigration Society, brought over five thousand emigrants from destitute Prussia. Supposedly British gold backed this venture. Sam Houston heard that rumor but shrugged his shoulders. The population of Texas was increasing; that was the important thing. The German emigrants crossed the Colorado and the Pedernales, extending the Texas frontier by almost a hundred miles. Two American companies contracted to locate families along the upper Trinity. New York and Chicago capital supplied the financial backing.

Again Texas was booming. The white population had grown from thirty thousand to over a hundred thousand. The President dismissed Congress and took temporary residence in Houston City, where he would receive political reports from the United States more promptly. He rose at daylight to muse on happenings in Washington and to pen his letters.

The United States had come to a political crossroads with Texas—the largest matter of contention. The Democratic choice would be James K. Polk, Sam's Tennessee friend, his successor in Congress. The Whigs nominated Henry Clay, the Kentuckian who had caused Jackson's defeat in 1824. The Democrats came out on a bold platform of "Oregon and Texas." The Whigs sought to avoid the Texas question.

Sam penned a stream of letters which added to the excitement of the Polk–Clay campaign. In one missive he discussed the advantages of independent sovereignty for Texas. European powers would help build a nation which would extend to the Pacific and envelop the northern states of Mexico, Chihuahua and Sonora. He pointed out that this prophecy about the future of this continent was no fanciful dream, but cold logic.

The letter went to General Murphy, who had just been relieved as United States chargé d'affaires to Texas. Sam knew Murphy would circulate the letter in Washington. He was sure, too, that the Democrats would wage a harder campaign as a result.

His "seed" planted, Sam left Houston City. The birth of Sam Houston, Junior overshadowed everything else. Margaret came through the confinement nicely. Proud of his fatherhood and his new status as a family man, Sam surrendered one of his last prejudices and was baptized in the Baptist Church. Thus Nancy Lea's last objection to her son-in-law was removed.

Sam drew plans for a larger house in Huntsville and handled all the building details himself. Presidential business took him to Washington-on-the-Brazos often, but he hurried back each time.

The new envoy from the United States, Andrew Jackson Donelson, had to travel to Huntsville to pay his respects. He received a warm personal welcome. President John Tyler had appointed Donelson as chargé d'affaires to the Lone Star nation. It was a calculated move. The Texas President's loyalty must be won back to the Union. If anyone could influence Houston, it was Andrew Jackson's favorite nephew.

But Sam refused to be overwhelmed.

"I am happy to confirm, sir," said Donelson, "that James K. Polk is the Democratic nominee for president. And our party's platform calls for annexation of Texas."

Sam knew that, of course. "And your platform," he said dryly, "calls for claiming Oregon Territory. Our English friends must be concerned."

"Let them be," declared Donelson. "It is time to make a clear-cut choice. North America will be either British or American. The nomination of Polk is our challenge to the world."

Sam's eyes gleamed. How like Andy Jackson this young man sounded! So a young Tennesseean was supposed to speak. But not an aging Texan.

"I remember Mr. Polk with much fondness," Sam said carefully. "He was my friend in state campaigns. And I have never forgotten how he championed me during that miserable Stanbury affair."

"He thinks highly of you." Donelson allowed himself to show eagerness. It would help us, sir, if your position on annexation was reestablished. Our people do not like the idea of semisecret negotiations between Texas and Europe."

He showed newspaper editorials to prove his point:

POLK—SLAVERY AND TEXAS. JAMES K. POLK AND GEORGE M. DALLAS, ONE FOR THE DEVIL AND ONE FOR THE GALLOWS.

Sam slowly shook his head. "I cannot say any more than I already have," he stated. "Our first loyalty is to Texas. Great Britain and France make solid proposals. They intervened with Mexico to secure the release of the Mier prisoners. They arranged a truce with Mexico. What does the United States offer?"

Sam did not wait for an answer, but smiled faintly and went on. "I read the Washington newspapers, sir. I know all about the charges that we are a bankrupt, backwoods people. Some of your leaders in Congress suggest that Texas resembles Botany Bay, that most of our early settlers were fugitives from American justice. I know that your Congress doesn't consider our public domain worth our national debt of six million dollars."

"That is one party speaking," Donelson argued. "The present administration is favorable to Texas. And if Mr. Polk is elected—"

"Let us hope he is elected," said Sam. "He is a worthy candidate." He rose to his feet. "You must win your election in the United States and squelch your rabble-rousing minorities. When you have done that—when you can bring something material to offer—we will give solemn consideration to your proposals." He gestured eloquently. "In the meantime, sir, Texas will struggle alone toward its place in the sun."

Sam sighed in pity as he watched Donelson ride away. He felt sorry for the young diplomat. How would Donelson report such coolness to Washington? He could not help wondering, either, how long this game of pairing off the European powers against the United States could be played.

At the moment, European representation in Texas was scarce. Charles Elliott's health had required that he take a rest in Hot Springs, Virginia. Count de Saligny, still chafing over the affair with the Austin innkeeper, was occupied in New Orleans. Sam hoped both of them would stay out of Texas until after the Polk–Clay election. He was especially grateful for Elliott's absence. The casual Englishman was a shrewd diplomat.

Sam considered the Texas political situation very satisfactory. He was leaving office shortly and Dr. Anson Jones would almost certainly be his successor. Jones, though somewhat colorless, was a capable man, familiar with every detail of the President's international politics. Sam went home to cast his vote for Jones. He lingered there, apparently more concerned with plans for a plantation home than with Polk's fate in the United States.

Andrew Donelson splashed down a muddy road to Huntsville with news of Democratic victory in the presidential race.

"If you are receptive, sir," proposed Jackson's nephew, "I will recommend the reopening of negotiations for annexation. We need not wait until Mr. Polk's inauguration next March."

"I am sure Mr. Jones will entertain any formal proposal," Sam said carefully.

Elliott also came hurrying into the Huntsville hills.

"I must advise you, sir," he informed Houston, "that England will go to any lengths to keep Texas out of the Union."

"There is no formal proposal from the United States," answered Houston, "just as there is no positive guarantee of your country's aid if we remain independent. As yet, sir, we are dealing only with intangibles."

Charles Elliott sighed. He knew when he had been

outmaneuvered. He went at once to Galveston and chartered the swiftest vessel in the harbor. The race was on between Great Britain and France on the one hand and the United States on the other. Texas was the prize.

Sam Houston made sure that Donelson learned about Captain Elliott's mission. Bedridden Andrew Jackson heard about the Englishman's trip, too. He summoned up the last reserves of his strength. A few Whig congressmen admitted their concern and wished that something could be done before Polk's inauguration. President Tyler thundered his denunciation of "rump" congressmen who would block the country's sentiments. The people of the United States had voted to annex Texas. Would they have to wait for a new congress to carry out their mandate? No, said Whig senators.

The annexation resolution was signed on March 1, 1845. Nineteen days later a steamer put into Galveston harbor with an official copy of the document.

Elliott and Saligny beat the dispatch to Washington-on-the-Brazos. They offered President Jones an alliance which guaranteed Texas sovereignty and military protection against any foreign power. Jones had been well coached. He politely agreed to let Texas voters take their choice.

Jones accepted the United States resolution as perfunctorily. He set a date for an early special election and formally announced three choices for Texas: to join the Union, to accept guaranteed sovereignty, or to reject both.

How would Texas vote? Andrew Jackson Donelson was anything but confident. He discovered, with some alarm, that not all Texans were thrilled by the prospect of statehood. At his urgent request, agents were sent to help him influence public opinion. But Captain Elliott and Count de Saligny were busy, too. Donelson wrote to Tennessee in despair. Sam Houston was taking no part in the debates, he reported. Anson Jones seemed to be entirely neutral. He reasoned that the people of Texas were waiting for word from Huntsville.

An extract from one of Houston's letters tormented his former fellow-Democrats: "Sentiment tells well in love matters . . . but the affairs of nations . . . have no soul and recognize no mentor but interest."

Sam, indeed, seemed entirely preoccupied. Perhaps the new home on Raven Hill was all that mattered. He spoke out finally, not as an official spokesman, but as a "citizen of Texas."

Of course he favored annexation. He reached the polls early and cast his vote for statehood. Standing outside afterward, he warmly greeted other voters. Nothing like this, he mused, had ever happened before. The people of one free nation, under no strain or duress, were voting to merge themselves with another.

The vote was going strong for statehood. As Sam turned away he wondered how soon Andy Jackson would learn the results.

It couldn't be too long, because already Donelson's couriers were riding toward the Hermitage. Jackson lay dying, but he rallied from the brink of the grave and spoke for hours of Texas and Houston. He sent for newspaper writers so the word would be spread throughout Tennessee and the Union that Sam Houston had kept every pledge he had ever made.

Jackson died two days later.

It was months before the process of annexation reached a climax. Meantime United States troops guarded the Texas border. The imminent war with Mexico need not be feared. On February 19, 1846, Dr. Anson Jones pronounced a simple benediction for a hectic historical decade.

"The Republic of Texas is no more."

Sam thought the words appropriate enough. He would have waxed more eloquent himself, but he carefully left this occasion to Anson Jones. They were scurrying around at Huntsville in happy preparation for another ceremony. Sam Houston was to be the first senator from Texas. Once again he traveled toward the Potomac. But under such different circumstances! He had just observed his fifty-fifth birthday. He was old as some men reckoned age, but he felt younger than he had in years as his own carriage whirled over these familiar roads. Margaret rode by his side. Another carriage followed with personal effects, a nurse, and the Houstons' second-born.

It was a long trip, yes. But the roadsides were strewn with roses.

★ 16

A Nation Divided

SAM HOUSTON FOUND MANY CHANGES IN WASHINGTON. A five-story inn rose where Brown's Tavern had stood. A new hotel across the avenue advertised private bathtubs. Both Henry Clay and Daniel Webster were fading as leaders of the Whig party, but John C. Calhoun still dominated Democratic congressmen. Almost every issue in the Senate evolved into a North versus South wrangle.

The senior senator from Texas avoided such controversy in his first session. He did not wish to antagonize either side, at least not until a certain matter was settled to Texas' advantage. By terms of the treaty signed at the end of the war with Mexico, the United States had acquired the Arizona and New Mexico territories. If the Rio Grande were the western boundary of Texas, as had been proclaimed with Sam's help before annexation, Santa Fe and other new settlements in the New Mexico territory were actually part of Texas.

Sam must have nursed a smile as he argued for Texas rights on the senate floor. He had first claimed such boundaries in an effort to win support for Texas annexation in the United States. Now he scented a chance to relieve Texas of its debts. The state had taken full responsibility for the obligations of the Lone Star republic. The state had also kept its public lands. The area of New

Mexico, argued Senator Houston, could not be organized into the territories of New Mexico and Colorado until Texas was indemnified for its "loss of territory."

Congress finally approved a settlement of ten million dollars, more than enough to pay the debts of the republic. Thus Texas began its statehood with a balance in its treasury and still owning some two hundred and twenty-five million acres of public lands. The senior senator was satisfied. Texas had indeed come into the Union "as a bride arrayed for the altar."

The settlement projected Sam even taller on the national scene. His colleague in the Senate was his longtime friend Thomas J. Rusk. They saw eye to eye on most issues, as they had agreed about war strategy in 1836. Rusk was willing to let Sam take the limelight in all senate debates.

Congress was deadlocked on the annexation of Oregon. The antislavery faction had yielded to public pressure and agreed to the admission of Texas as a slaveholding state. Supposedly the South had thus added two precious votes in the Senate. Oregon, therefore, must be a "free state," restoring the balance of power in Congress.

There was one flaw to such a political analysis. John C. Calhoun should have expected it. Had the South Carolina senator forgotten those hectic campaigns of the 1820's? Didn't Calhoun recall that Sam Houston had echoed Andy Jackson's strong opposition to secession? Jackson was dead now, but the onetime Tennessee congressman had become a senator. And Sam's conception of the Union hadn't changed in twenty years.

It had been that long. Sam faced his fellow senators on August 14, 1848. His carefully chosen words resounded over the entire country.

He knew neither North nor South, he said, but "only

the Union." He believed that he occupied his seat as "a representative of the whole American people." He wanted the flag carried westward. He had devoted his life to that ambition. He wanted Oregon accepted into the Union and the question of slavery left to settlers of the Oregon Territory.

Dismay swept the southern senators, then blazing anger. No slaves had been transported across the Rockies to Oregon. The settlers were sure to vote for a "free" status. So would other territories forming in the borning West.

Cries of "traitor" came from Calhoun and other southern leaders. Denunciations were printed in southern newspapers. "Houston is a falling star—a Lucifer descending from the heavens!"

Protesting letters poured up from Texas—threats, too. Sam paced the streets of Washington with his greatcoat pulled up around his bared head. He was grateful that Margaret had not accompanied him to the Potomac for this second session. Another child was expected shortly; besides, the Potomac winters were too severe. She could choose her climate in Texas: the salty coastal clime or the pleasant mildness of Raven Hill. She was doing well; every letter said so.

And, happily, she was being spared this latest storm. Better that he face it alone. He was case-hardened to such revilement, or should be. Blackguard, a modern Judas! He strode to his desk in the Senate with tight lips and sat stiffly with unbowed head. He had voiced his convictions. He was still pursuing the star which had been his goal since childhood, the western star.

Every day he read that he had blasted his chances for national political success. He had turned himself overnight into a man without following, except for the loyal

Rusk. He dared to be neither Yankee nor Southerner in this showdown fight to decide America's political future. Still another time, he stood alone in a crowd.

Then, one drizzly night, a familiar voice broke in on his grim thoughts. "Houston! My lad, it's great to see you again."

Sam's heart leaped with joy. Junius Booth, the venerable actor, his loyal champion and critic!

And Junius brought welcome news. Daniel Webster was coming out of semiretirement to plead Sam's cause. There must be compromise about Oregon. The South must yield on this issue as New England had finally relented in the annexation of Texas.

"Webster will make a great speech," Booth said enthusiastically. "He is old and tired but he will be at his best." The aged thespian, however, was still a critic at heart. "Webster is a good showman, once he gets over his stiff beginning. Would he had more of your dramatic flair, my friend. Webster could never face the Senate in an Indian vest and Spanish spurs. He can never take on a new character. He is a New Englander, first, last, and always." The great actor smiled fondly at Sam. "And what are you, General? You have the whole country wondering. Are you Southerner or Indian?"

Sam's eyes twinkled. He always found Booth irresistible. "The first Americans south of the Red River were described as Texicans," Sam said. "Born and reared in the United States but matured in Texas. Does that make sense?"

Booth nodded. "To a man who will think beyond the end of his nose, yes. But our congressmen aren't noted for their long-range vision."

This was the great debate of 1850. The Union lay in the balance. Neither northern agitators nor southern secessionists meant to give an inch. Were there enough "moderate" congressmen to force some sort of compromise?

Sam believed there were. Another great figure was coming out of the shadows—Clay. Like Webster, he was casting off his Whig affiliation in his last political gesture. Some of their party would follow, reflected Houston. Now could he win over a few reluctant Democrats? He selected his prospects and pursued them one by one. This was not unlike politics of the 1820's. A new coalition was shaping up. Sam's role was like the one he had performed under Jackson. He must be the man behind the scenes.

He threw himself into this campaign. In the first place, he believed in it heart and soul. "The Federal Union, it must be preserved." So Andrew Jackson had answered southern secessionists a generation before.

And, second, here loomed the opportunity for personal triumph. A new western "strong man" could emerge out of this conflict, as Jackson had leaped up in the 1820's. It wouldn't be Clay, so near to dying; nor Webster, turning his back on his home state, his lifelong friends. There would be no healing the wounds if Webster spoke.

Clay came first. Frail and tottering, the Kentucky Whig leader spoke through two sessions. Then Webster came to the rostrum. He delivered an oration which left even Booth speechless, and the Whig party in shambles. The Compromise of 1850 was voted. Disunion was averted. Huzzahs sounded for the two dying men. Webster and Clay had won their last fights. But didn't Sam Houston hold the spoils of victory in his own two hands? The party which had blocked annexation of

Texas was scattered to the four winds. And talk spread among the Democrats that their best presidential choice was the talented senator from Texas.

Sam traveled back to Texas by railroad coach. The trip took only eight days. There were no limits to the development of America, provided North and South could settle their squabble about slavery. Imagine traveling from Washington to Houston in only eight days!

A letter from Congressman Andrew Johnson of Tennessee was waiting for him. Johnson asked permission to put Sam's name in nomination at the 1852 Democratic convention.

Sam put off answering to buy another plantation near Independence. This was higher country than either Huntsville or Houston. Margaret might be more comfortable there during the summer months.

Nancy Lea sniffed. "Must she have a home for every season of the year?"

Sam smiled at his mother-in-law. "You would not allow her to come to Texas until I promised full comforts," he said. "I am doing my best."

Would the Democrats nominate Houston for the presidency? Sam decided not. Party rules required a two-thirds majority for nomination. There was no mistaking the intentions of delegates from the southern states. They could not dominate the convention but they could prevent any one candidate from getting a majority. Voting went on for ballot after ballot.

Some compromise had to be reached or the dying Whig party might win after all. Franklin Pierce of New Hampshire was offered as a compromise candidate. Sam's delegates accepted, believing that a New Englander would prove a "moderate." They were wrong. Pierce turned out to be pro-southern. The ranks of the "moderates" grew thinner.

Most transferred their allegiance to the new party, the Republicans. Sam was sorely tempted. The Republicans appeared to be dominated by the West. John C. Frémont was named as their first candidate. He was no great political leader but at least he believed in westward expansion.

But something held Sam back. Was it a lifetime of loyalty? Was it a sudden indifference to personal achievement? Or was it the conviction that the Democratic majority would finally adjust its differences and merge behind a single standard bearer?

Something of all three things, he decided. The presidency didn't seem as important any more. He was in his sixties, now. He had a large family, and personal holdings scattered over two hundred miles of Texas soil. And his concern about Texas was getting to be an obsession. Maybe he was wasting his time in Washington, frittering away his energies when his real duty was back home.

The 1856 convention convinced Sam. Out of the wrangling, debating and shifting of voices came the nomination of still another weak candidate. The southern minority wouldn't allow a strong man to flex his muscles. The eventual choice of James Buchanan pleased no one. The northern Democrats left the convention muttering and planning a showdown fight in 1860. The western delegates were as disgruntled. Next time they would vote for a Unionist candidate or walk out. The Democratic party, decided Sam, would split into no less than three segments. Buchanan won the election, but the wiser Democrats knew this was their last victory.

There would never be another compromise with the

militant men from the southern states. If they wanted the walls falling around them, then so it must be.

Sam acted in sudden, dramatic decision.

He was going home. He was leaving the Senate to seek the governorship of Texas.

The Union was breaking apart. Secession was inevitable. Texas must again shift for itself and avoid formal alliance with the Carolinas, Georgia, Alabama and Mississippi. If worse came to worst, Texas must resume its status as an independent republic.

★ 17

The Last Battleground

THIS WAS 1857, AND HOT, DREARY AUGUST. IT HAD BEEN almost twenty-five years since Sam rode a nondescript roan pony to Texas. Then he had borrowed a razor to shave and had required Adolphus Sterne's bounty to open an unpretentious law office.

Now his personal quests were over. The road to Texas had led to a domestic happiness beyond his most eager dream. Margaret waited impatiently at Huntsville. The house on Raven Hill was alive with cheerful, busy children. Sam, Junior, handsome at fourteen; Nannie, just a bit younger; Maggie, a snaggle-toothed seven-year-old; and Andrew Jackson Houston, now three—here was a family to delight any man.

A statesman turned sixty, a man twice president of a republic, also a congressman and a senator—why did he want to be elected governor of Texas! That question flew from lip to lip when Sam announced his candidacy against Hardin Runnels, the choice of the Democratic convention.

Turncoat, demagogue, would-be dictator—the same old words were turned upon him again. Hadn't Houston gone to the Senate as a Democrat? And now he would try to defeat the nominee of that party. His term in the Senate wouldn't expire until 1859. Why couldn't he be satisfied with the position he held?

Sam had good and valid reasons. The Democratic party had become the party of secession. He must fight it somewhere, and a wise general chose his own battleground. Texans would listen to him.

The party in his home state was dominated by southern radicals, too. A former South Carolinian, Louis Wigfall, had been chosen to replace the deceased Tom Rusk as Texas' junior senator. Runnels was the overwhelming choice of that party. Sam's assault took the Democratic camp by surprise, but the radical group quickly formed ranks for a bitter fight. They would get it. Sam Houston was a formidable foe even if he scorned party, press or general electioneering paraphernalia and campaigned simply on his own name.

The southern radicals elected their man by some nine thousand votes—32,552 to 23,628. Most Texans weren't ready to believe Sam's warning that the Democratic road could lead only to disunion.

But it was not a disastrous defeat. Sam accepted it philosophically. He hadn't started his campaign in time. Every one of the odds had been against him, too. He must summon back his powers of patience and wait for events to bear out his predictions.

He returned to Washington to finish out his term, to watch at firsthand the inevitable approach of secession, to lay his plans for 1859.

Actually he had gained a strategic advantage. He had set Texans to studying national events and appraising their other state leaders. Every speech Louis Wigfall delivered in the Senate confirmed Sam's charges that the regular Texas Democrats were allied with southern radicals.

Sam fashioned many trinkets with his jackknife as he listened to the bitter harangue in Congress. He spent his evenings writing letters to Margaret and his friends in Texas. Let the state party be warned about the next election.

He left Washington with some sadness. It was March, 1859; the Potomac countryside was just awakening to spring. Thirty-five years ago, reflected Sam, he had seen the capital in ashes. Would war sweep Washington again? He did not doubt it. The new Republican party grew stronger every day. Its leadership was heeding new voices from the West. The Democrats were hopelessly divided. Sam heard talk of two separate conventions. If such a thing happened, a Republican would occupy the White House. No matter who it might be, Sam would not envy him. He no longer nourished presidential ambitions for himself. Ahead of him was one last fight—to pull Texas out of the bitter wrangle between North and South. There was only one way to accomplish this—run for governor of Texas.

He started campaigning immediately, driving himself hard through the summer's heat. He likened Hardin Runnels to David Burnet, this campaign to the presidential race in 1841. And, at times, Sam blazed out denunciations as bitter as those he had hurled against Burnet.

In Lockhart, a small town near the capital city, Sam rose to speak, wearing a linen duster about his shoulders. On the same platform was a prominent Texas jurist, W. S. Oldham, bearing several lawbooks. Oldham had advertised his intention of speaking in favor of Runnels.

"There is Judge Oldham," roared Sam. "He has some books with him, but they are not the same bankbooks he stole and sank in the Arkansas River."

At another stop Sam was challenged for his "treachery" to Texas and the South.

"What!" he shouted. "Houston a traitor to Texas!" He unbuttoned his duster and showed his bare chest. "I carry a scar here." He hobbled a few steps about the platform. "I still limp from the wound of San Jacinto." He glared around him. "As for my senate record, I stand opposed to the Black Republicans and the equally dangerous fanatics of the South."

He gestured to the courthouse. "A flag once floated over those walls, a flag of decency and honor and courage. The Lone Star flag! No man did more to raise it than I, and no man struggled harder to make sure it was lowered with dignity and solemn promise of better things." He paused and his eyes gleamed. "If need be," he said quietly, "that flag can be raised again."

Neither northern nor southern, but *Texan. Texican*—the more he used the old term, the more it appealed to him. There were more towns to visit, more platforms to mount. He urged the driver of his open carriage to a faster pace.

He came finally to Columbia, which had served the republic as a temporary seat of government. Local officials demurred about letting such a controversial candidate hold his meeting on the courthouse steps. Sam accepted the rebuff. He turned to the gathering crowd.

"Follow me to those oaks," he shouted, indicating a thick grove nearby. Here had once stood the frame building he had occupied as first president of Texas. "I have every right to speak from there. I have stained those oaks with my own blood."

He made an impassioned speech, then the carriage whirled back along the dusty road to Huntsville. Sam cast his vote in his home precinct and then offered his excuses to Margaret.

"I have been away too much," he said. His duster

was soiled; his trousers were bagged, his boots caked with mud. "I am a sad sight," he confessed ruefully. "I am surprised that you will let me into the house."

Margaret smiled down at him. "You were a worse sight when I first saw you. Then you were stained with blood and could hardly stand on your own feet."

"Yes," he recalled softly. "I would have fallen on the dock if it hadn't been for you." He sighed. "And I think I would have collapsed during this campaign if I hadn't known you were waiting here."

He closed his eyes and fell sound asleep in his chair. Margaret and the children tiptoed carefully around him —until almost seven o'clock, that is.

Margaret shook him awake then. The first returns were in. Sam came wide-awake at once. His lined features relaxed and his eyes gleamed. By midnight the trend was certain. Texas had welcomed Sam Houston home.

Eighteen years had passed since Sam traveled to Austin to begin his second term as president of the Texas republic. Conditions had changed; a comfortable mansion awaited the new governor and his family. The house was only four years old. The chief executive could cross a single street and reach his offices in the capitol. Margaret struggled breathlessly with all the problems of moving. The children's schooling must not be interrupted. Arrangements must be made for care of four Houston residences.

Sam flouted inaugural customs. He spoke from the capitol steps, not in the legislative chambers. He wanted all of Texas to hear what he had to say.

"When Texas united her destiny with that of the United States, she entered not into the North or the

South. Her connection was *national.* The Union was intended to be a perpetuity."

Then Sam set out to occupy Texans with their own problems. There were many things to be done. Some departments of government should be overhauled. The Ranger corps must be strengthened. There were Comanches to subdue in the West, and troublesome Mexican bandits plagued southern settlements. Sam counted on the United States Army regulars sent to subdue the Mexican raiders. He was particularly impressed with Colonel Robert E. Lee, who quietly professed his own concern about national affairs. He did not believe in slavery, though he was a native of Virginia.

Colonel Lee, mused Sam, would be a welcome addition to the ranks of adopted Texans.

But the political bitterness of 1860 converged upon the busy governor. Former Governor Runnels led the Texas delegation to the Democratic convention. There was no doubt how he stood. Texas would support only a candidate acceptable to the South. Texans led the southern bolters who refuted Stephen A. Douglas. John C. Breckinridge was nominated in a rump convention.

The Republicans proved more astute. They rejected all leading abolitionists to nominate a compromise candidate. At least they hoped Abraham Lincoln of Illinois would prove so.

They were wrong. Lincoln's views about slavery were mild enough, but he had delivered a ringing speech about national unity. A house divided against itself, he said, could not stand.

Still another party formed in a hurry, the National Unionists. John Bell of Tennessee became a fourth entry in the most crucial campaign in American history.

Houston was disappointed. The Unionists, he felt,

might have won with a stronger candidate. He announced his support of Bell but continued to busy himself with state and domestic matters. He had been reconciled to this crisis since 1857.

The election was a quiet one in Texas. Breckinridge polled 47,000 votes and Bell 15,000. None were counted for Douglas or Lincoln.

The national picture took positive image. Lincoln, with two-fifths of the popular vote, claimed a good majority in the electoral college. Southern firebrands had warned that their states must secede if Lincoln was elected. What should Texas do now?

Governor Houston spoke out calmly.

"Mr. Lincoln has been elected on a sectional issue. If he expects to maintain that sectional issue during his administration, it is well that we should know it. If he intends to administer the government with equality and fairness, we should know that. Let us wait and see."

But events moved too quickly. Southern senators left Washington in a blaze of eloquence. Among them was Louis Wigfall of Texas. South Carolina seceded on December 20, 1860. Other states followed. Governor Houston was engulfed with demands for a special session of the legislature. He delayed action, hoping the excitement would ebb. Instead it swelled higher. Southern zealots laid plans for a special convention to decide the future of Texas.

Houston chose to deal with the legislature. He called a special session for January 20, 1861.

A visitor the same day caused further sad reflection. Colonel Lee was resigning from the United States Army. His native state of Virginia was leaving the Union. Despite his personal feelings about slavery and secession, he cast his lot with Virginia.

★ 18

The Last Fight

THE CONFEDERACY WAS ALREADY FORMED. SOME PEOPLE expected Abraham Lincoln, the man who had been elected president, to sit idly by while his nation fell apart at the seams. But Lincoln did all a man could who would not actually take office until March 4.

One of his couriers reached Austin in early February, bearing special dispatches for Governor Houston. The legislature had already assembled for its special session. Its sentiments were all too obvious.

"Lincoln's election is regrettable, but it is no cause for the immediate secession of Texas," said the governor's message. "Let the record of no one rash act blur Texas' pages in history."

The members paid respectful attention to the message, but Sam realized that their opinions were not influenced. Otherwise he would not have given Lincoln's secret offer another thought. Under the circumstances, however, he read the message carefully, then sent for his most loyal political followers.

They met in the living room of the mansion. Usually this room was filled with family activities in the evenings. After supper twelve-year-old Maggie would write letters for her father while the others studied their lessons or told Sam about the events of the day. This night, under

Margaret's gentle prodding, they helped arrange chairs for the governor's guests, then withdrew.

It was a cold, damp evening. Sam lit a log fire. Margaret brought refreshments, then slipped away. Sam faced his friends.

"Today," he said gravely, "I received this offer from Abraham Lincoln."

He slowly and impressively read Mr. Lincoln's proposals. The President-elect was already in tacit control of the North's military might. If Governor Houston would hold Texas out of the Confederacy, Mr. Lincoln would send seventy-five thousand troops in support. He would commission Sam a major-general and appoint him commander of Union armies in the Southwest.

"It could be done," Sam declared. "The convention will vote Texas out of the Union if we don't. But I could call out the Texas Rangers and declare martial law. We have several companies ready for immediate action and are better armed than at any time in our history."

His listeners smiled. For months now Governor Houston had wangled rifles and powder out of the United States Government. He had conscripted several new Ranger companies and those units were stationed within quick striking distance of Austin!

"There are loyal garrisons in San Antonio, Fort Clark, Fort McIntosh and a dozen other forts," Governor Houston continued. "There are enough fighting men available to hold Texas until Mr. Lincoln's reinforcements arrive."

He slowly folded Lincoln's letter.

"Well, gentlemen?" he asked crisply.

His sharp eyes settled on J. W. Throckmorton. This handsome young man was on his way to greater things. Sam had already chosen him as a likely successor. Throckmorton hesitated only a moment.

"Can we hold Texas by force in all conscience, General?" His lips twitched. "I am tempted, yes, sir. Every man here is. But that is—well, sir, I hadn't given it a serious thought."

"There would be civil war in Texas, General."

The soft reminder came from Elihu Pease.

"There will be civil war all over America," snapped Sam. He lifted Lincoln's letter. "Does this sound like a president who will let the southern states go their separate ways in peace? I tell you, the South has underestimated Lincoln. They have always failed to respect a man who did not measure up to their so-called social graces. They have never recognized the abilities of men from the frontier. And Lincoln is out of the woods, the crossroads. He believes in an America as we believe in it, a changing America."

"Yes, General," nodded Pease. "There will be civil war all over America. But it will not be on my conscience or yours."

Pease had served as governor himself. He had sponsored legislation to establish a public school system and had encouraged the building of railroads and highways. Sam considered him one of the state's outstanding citizens.

"What are *your* sentiments, General?" asked Benjamin Epperson.

George W. Paschal nodded. "You read us Mr. Lincoln's offer and asked for our reactions. What course have you decided to take?"

Sam hesitated. "None," he admitted finally. He heaved a deep sigh. "I have sat here and struggled with my own desires all this afternoon. I am sixty-eight years old, gentlemen. I cannot decide such a thing on my own. I came to Texas alone but knowing what I meant to achieve. I let no man advise me and I would have turned deaf ears to any man who would have dissuaded me. But I was younger then and time was in my favor. Now time is against me."

His sharp eyes swept their troubled faces. "And so are you," he said tonelessly.

Throckmorton was the first to stir. "Yes, General," he said softly, "we are against you. We can't follow you—this far."

"That is enough," declared Sam. He trembled from head to foot. "But if I were thirty years younger," he said hoarsely, "I wouldn't hesitate. I would hold Texas out of the Confederacy by force or arms or any way I could. I would send out a clarion call all over the West—to California, to Oregon. This is no more their war than it is ours. I would proclaim another nation on this same spot where the Lone Star republic gave up its existence. But this new republic would sweep from the Mississippi and the Rio Grande to the Pacific. I would leave New England and the South to fight their senseless war alone. England and France would help me. They did before and they would again."

He gestured helplessly with both hands. "Some men had that dream for Texas twenty-five years ago," he recalled. "They had the dream too early. It was impractical then. It would have served posterity no good purpose. But now—now—I have the dream too late."

He turned to face the fire. "Thank you for coming, gentlemen," he said politely, "and for giving an old man your full consideration."

Throckmorton answered for the distressed group. "Thank you for asking us, General. No greater compliment was ever paid us."

Sam turned as the last guest left the room. "Would you ask Margaret to come in, please?"

She found him writing at a small table before the fire. "Must you work, dear, at this hour?"

He finished a sentence, then looked up with sheepish apology. "I didn't hear you, my dear."

"Mr. Throckmorton said you wanted me."

"Yes," nodded Sam. He sighed and stretched his long legs. "We must be moving soon. I know you dislike interrupting the children's schooling, but it can't be helped this time. We are going home."

"And which house—is home?"

"That is for you to decide," he said calmly. His eyes twinkled. "You may want to give the matter some deliberation, for this time we go home to stay."

Texas voted for secession. On March 4 a convention declared Texas a part of the Confederacy and ordered all state officials to take the oath of allegiance to the new country on March 16 at high noon.

A great crowd gathered to watch the ceremony. At two minutes past noon the secretary of the convention called for the Governor of Texas to swear his allegiance to the Confederacy.

"Sam Houston," called R. T. Brownrigg.

There was no answer.

"Sam Houston! Sam Houston!"

Silence. Not a man stirred. Hundreds of eyes watched the door. Would he come striding through that portal, dressed in some colorful costume, standing head and shoulders above anyone present? Would he stalk forward to the rostrum and throw back his shaggy head and roar out his challenge?

"Sam Houston! Sam Houston!"

The secretary turned to the presiding officer for instructions. The governor had been summoned five times and had not responded. What now?

The chairman gathered several key figures around him. Their decision was that the office of governor was vacant. Lieutenant-Governor Edward Clark would accede to the office automatically.

Once more, Sam Houston had abruptly abandoned the center of a stage. But this time he went without fanfare.

Margaret decided their destination. Huntsville first, then Cedar Point. The war had begun before the children were settled in their new surroundings. Among the dignitaries who witnessed the shelling of Fort Sumter was Louis Wigfall, former United States Senator from Texas.

President Lincoln called for volunteers. The new Confederate government had dared to assault a United States arsenal. War would have come anyhow, Sam said calmly. War had actually begun with secession.

That came in April. June brought Sam, Junior home from Texas Military Academy. The tall, slim youth conferred anxiously with his mother. There were tears in her eyes as she listened to his wish.

"Discuss it with your father," she insisted gently. "He must know about your feelings."

Sam offered no objection. "I cannot dictate his loyalties. Each man must set his own course. He goes with my blessing."

And off marched the oldest Houston son with the Second Texas Cavalry. The son of Sam Houston in a Confederate uniform! The entire family visited the young soldier at Galveston Island. Six months later he was wounded at Shiloh and sent home.

For a time Margaret nursed two invalids. The younger Sam recovered first. The father later rallied enough to visit the city named in his honor, to stir up speculation that he would seek the governorship in 1863. He allowed the rumor to spread for a while, then announced his firm refusal.

He had left home for the last time. Home was more precious than ever as death grew closer. Sam, Junior returned to the front. A new piano decorated the parlor.

Sam felt well enough to deliver an address in March, 1863. The words he spoke seemed to some a reversal of his former stand: "Let us bid defiance to all the hosts that our enemies can bring against us. Can Lincoln subjugate a people thus resolved? No!"

His listeners applauded wildly, but the Raven intended no approval of the Confederacy. He gloried when Texas repulsed Yankee invaders at Galveston and Sabine Pass. He always gloried in a Texas triumph.

A cough had plagued him since early 1860 and he traveled to Sour Lake for mineral baths. A letter from Margaret cut short his treatment. "Temple talks about you every day." He was the child born in the governor's mansion. "Nannie is visiting at Independence. Sam, Junior is home on furlough but gone again, on a visit to Mexico this time. Maggie sends her love as does Andrew." . . .

Cough or no cough, Sam Houston started for home. Margaret put him to bed as soon as he arrived. There was no doubt of his ailment—pneumonia.

The next day he fell into a drugged-like sleep. The

family gathered close around him. He stirred once, and managed a weak whisper.

"Texas . . . Texas . . . Margaret . . ."

And then Sam Houston was still. The man who had touched the stars and felt them change to dust was dead.

Suggested Further Reading

Adams, Samuel Hopkins. *Santa Fe Trail.* Random House, New York, 1951.

Blair, Walter. *David Crockett, Frontier Hero.* Coward-McCann, Inc., New York, 1955.

Burt, Olive. *John Charles Fremont: Trail Marker of the Old West.* Julian Messner, Inc., New York, 1955.

Carroll, Curt. *San Jacinto.* The Steck Company, Austin, 1955.

Emery, Guy. *Robert E. Lee.* Julian Messner, Inc., New York, 1951.

Garst, Shannon. *James Bowie.* Julian Messner, Inc., New York, 1955.

Henry, Will. *The Texas Rangers.* Random House, New York, 1957.

Hoff, Carol. *Johnny Texas.* Follett Publishing Co., Chicago, 1950.

———. *Johnny Texas on the San Antonio Road.* Follett Publishing Co., Chicago, 1953.

James, Bessie. *Six Foot Six.* Bobbs-Merrill Co., Indianapolis, 1931.

James, Bessie and Marquis. *Courageous Heart.* Bobbs-Merrill Co., Indianapolis, 1934.

Kieran, Margaret and John. *James John Audubon.* Random House, New York, 1954.

McCracken, Harold. *Winning of the West.* Garden City Books, Garden City, New York, 1955.

Nolan, Jeannette Covert. *Andrew Jackson.* Julian Messner, Inc., New York, 1949.

Shapiro, Irwin. *Yankee Thunder.* Julian Messner. Inc., New York, 1955.

Index

About the Author

CURTIS BISHOP was born in Tennessee, moved to Texas in his youth, and still lives there. His writing career started early, and by the time he was sixteen he was a newspaper reporter and sports writer. He is the author of more than 30 books for adults and young people dealing with a variety of subjects: sports, westerns, history and biography.